*The Royal Academy and The Times
present
Old Master Paintings
from the Thyssen-Bornemisza Collection*

*The Royal Academy of Arts is grateful to
Her Majesty's Government for agreeing to indemnify
the exhibition under the National Heritage Act 1980
and to the Museums and Galleries Commission
for their help in arranging this indemnity.*

Old Master Paintings from the Thyssen-Bornemisza Collection

Catalogue by
David Ekserdjian

Edited by
MaryAnne Stevens

Electa
Royal Academy of Arts

Dates of the exhibition
18 March – 12 June 1988

Acknowledgments
Dr Lorne Campbell
Dr Joanna Cannon
David Davies
Professor Francis Haskell
Dr Ivan Gaskell
Simon de Pury
Timothy Wilson

Cover illustration
Cat. 27
Hans Holbein the Younger
King Henry VIII

CONTENTS

SPONSOR'S PREFACE

Newspapers, like great art, have the power to stretch the boundaries of knowledge and understanding, cutting across geographical and political divides in the pursuit of excellence. The Times *is committed to that pursuit and prides itself on being an accurate voice for public opinion in this country. As such, it has always placed great importance on the arts and on recognising the public need for access to the great art treasures of the world. When* The Times *learned of a series of art exchanges between Russia and Baron Thyssen, a man known for his remarkable and unique art collection, it was able to look beyond the story: the seeds were sown for an exhibition which without doubt would make a major contribution to the art world in this country.*

In the autumn of 1987 The Times *approached the Baron about exhibiting part of his magnificent private collection in London. He not only agreed but extended the list to include other famous works. The result is an exhibition of some of the finest examples of European masterpieces ever to be seen in London.*

The Times *is honoured and delighted to be able to express its commitment to the arts in this way, and takes pleasure in joining the Royal Academy to present this splendid exhibition.*

Charles Wilson
Editor of The Times

PRESIDENT'S FOREWORD

After the great success of the exhibition of Modern Masters *from the* Thyssen-Bornemisza Collection *at the Royal Academy in 1984, Baron Hans Heinrich Thyssen-Bornemisza is once more demonstrating his outstanding generosity by allowing us to show for the first time at the Royal Academy, and for only the second time in London, a fine selection of his great collection of Old Master paintings. Begun by his father some fifty years ago and significantly extended by the present Baron, the collection has been for many years on view to the public at Villa Favorita, near Lugano in Switzerland, where indeed it is one of the outstanding attractions of that country.*

Baron Thyssen has always believed that great works of art should be seen by as many people as possible. In pursuit of this belief he has allowed distinguished parts of his collection to be lent to numerous museums and galleries in North America, Japan and in Western and Eastern Europe. In recent years, he has also mounted in Lugano several memorable exhibitions, particularly of great masterpieces from Soviet and Hungarian museums, as well as a beautiful exhibition of works by Goya from private collections in Spain. His collection is certainly used with exemplary enterprise and imagination.

Obviously, our greatest thanks are due to Baron Thyssen for once more sharing his collection with us. Its masterpieces by Holbein, Memling, Dürer and Caravaggio, to mention only four, will give us the greatest pleasure. However, we are also especially grateful to The Times *who suggested that we hold this exhibition and who have most generously agreed to act as sponsors. We welcome our renewed cooperation with them, which we hope will continue in the future. The paintings were selected by Norman Rosenthal, Exhibitions Secretary of the Royal Academy, together with the art historian David Ekserdjian. We are greatly indebted to David Ekserdjian for having agreed at short notice to write the introduction and catalogue notes on the paintings. We also extend our deep gratitude to Professor Francis Haskell and to Dr Lorne Campbell, Dr Joanna Cannon, David Davies and Dr Ivan Gaskell for their invaluable advice on specific notes in the catalogue. Irene Martin, the Baron's curator and Emil Bosshard, his restorer, have also provided much advice and assistance.*

Some of the Baron's great masterpieces, notably the Carpaccio and the Ghirlandaio, were unable to come to London, principally for conservation reasons. We can only recommend visitors to this exhibition not to miss any opportunity to visit the collection in its beautiful site on the shore of Lake Lugano.

Roger de Grey
President, Royal Academy of Arts

AN INTRODUCTION TO THE THYSSEN-BORNEMISZA COLLECTION OF OLD MASTER PAINTINGS

The Old Master collection of Baron Hans Heinrich Thyssen-Bornemisza, both in terms of its quality and in terms of its size (approximately 570 paintings at the last count) is the greatest private collection of old masters in the world apart from that of Her Majesty the Queen. It is hard to see how it will ever be rivalled in the future, far less surpassed. The collection was first exhibited at the Neue Pinakothek in Munich 1930, and in the intervening years both it and its fame have grown, so that there is now an understandable temptation to take it for granted. This temptation should be resisted, however, not only because the collection has such a fascinating and unexpected history, but also because the final chapter of that history is far from having been written.

The major royal collections, of which the Queen's pictures are the last surviving example, were the products of acquisition by many generations of crowned heads. The great holdings of museums such as the Louvre, the Prado and the Hermitage all came into being in this way. By contrast, the Thyssen-Bornemisza Collection has been entirely assembled in this century and is the achievement of two men. It was started by the present Baron's father, Heinrich (fig. 1), and continued by the present Baron after his father's death in 1947. Furthermore, the paintings collection is only one among many, although undoubtedly the most impressive as well as the most extensive, and is complemented by other outstanding collections including those of oriental carpets, mediaeval ivories and Renaissance jewels. Nor should it be forgotten that the present Baron has considerably expanded the range of the paintings collection, so that it is no longer exclusively devoted to Old Masters.

In 1984 the Royal Academy mounted a substantial exhibition of Modern Masters from the Thyssen-Bornemisza Collection. Particular strengths were the German Expressionists, the pre- and post-war Americans, and contemporary British painters. The Baron's admiration for the works of Lucian Freud (shared, interestingly enough, by the current custodian of another major, if dwindling private collection, the Duke of Devonshire), has led to two portrait commissions, one of which is on show in the present exhibition (fig. 2). It shows the Baron in front of a relatively recent acquisition, Watteau's *Pierrot content* (cat. 52), which was purchased in 1977. Freud only knew the canvas in reproduction, and in view of his use of it for *Large Interior, W11. (after Watteau)*, it is tempting to suppose that he imagined it was considerably more substantial than it actually is. Another entire collection formed by the Baron, and perhaps inevitably less well known in this country, comprises nineteenth-century American paintings.

Before charting the evolution of the Thyssen-Bornemisza Collection of Old Masters, however, it is worth briefly outlining the history of the family behind it. The family fortune was established by the present Baron's grandfather, August Thyssen, who was born in 1842 and died in 1926. He was a great industrialist, who owned an iron and steel works at Mülheim on the Rhine at a time when both prices and profits soared. When his business interests expanded into France, he met and befriended Auguste Rodin, half a dozen of whose works he eventually owned. Otherwise, and in spite of his considerable wealth, he was no collector: the walls of his home, Schloss Landsberg, were hung with copies of old masters, rather than originals.

His third and youngest son, Heinrich (1875-1947), more than made amends for his father's indifference to art. Although he was a financier and a banker, art was the passion of his life, and he was the friend of such great art historians as Wilhelm Bode and Max J. Friedlander. He took a Ph.D. at London University and then, after his marriage to the daughter of an impoverished Hungarian aristocrat, Baron Bornemisza, and the latter's American wife, he settled in his bride's native land. He became a naturalised Hungarian, was adopted by his

1

2

father-in-law, and took the title of Baron Thyssen-Bornemisza. He bought Schloss Rohoncz, after which the collection was originally named, and lived there until 1919 when Béla Kun and the Communists came to power. Heinrich and his family fled to Holland, where his youngest child, the present Baron, was born at Scheveningen in 1921. In 1932 the first Baron Thyssen-Bornemisza bought the Villa Favorita at Castagnola (fig. 3), a small village on Lake Lugano which has now effectively been swallowed up by Lugano, from Prince Friedrich Leopold of Prussia. To the exquisite seventeenth-century house, with its idyllic lakeside situation, he added in 1937 a picture gallery, which is reached from the house by a long corridor. The villa became the Thyssen-Bornemisza home, and is still lived in by the family, although the present Baron prefers to occupy a modern flat hung with twentieth-century pictures on an upper floor as opposed to the extremely formal apartments decorated in various period styles—Gothic, Louis XV, and so on—by his father. From the first, however, the gallery was arranged with all the meticulous discipline of a museum, and even divided into larger, central, primary galleries and smaller side rooms on the standard Beaux-Arts model. The collection formed by the present Baron's father was built up predominantly in the 1920s and 1930s, at a time when many more great pictures were still in private hands than is now the case, and when prices—even allowing for inflation—were far more modest than those of today. Baron Heinrich began by collecting the works of his first love, the Early German School, and acquired a number of remarkable paintings. Two that stand out are Hans Holbein the Younger's *King Henry VIII* (cat. 27) and Albrecht Dürer's *Christ Among the Doctors* (cat. 19), both of which came from illustrious collections. The former belonged to Earl Spencer, and was acquired from Althorp in 1934, the latter came from Palazzo Barberini in Rome the following year. Other great names such as Albrecht Altdorfer (cat. 1) and Hans Baldung Grien (cat. 3) are also represented, and in addition there are seven pictures by Lucas Cranach the Elder and his son Hans (cat. 14) which stand out as the most formidable ensemble in the entire collection. They were all purchased before the Second World War, and the German School has proved to be an area where the present Baron has not significantly extended the collection, more

3

4

on account of lack of availability than lack of inclination. One notable exception has been the purchase of additional fragments of what must once have been an immense *Crucifixion* by the fifteenth-century painter Dirk Bagaert to join those already in the collection.

A taste for German Renaissance painting led naturally enough to the Early Netherlandish School, and here too astonishing acquisitions were made. From among them, two again stand out: Jan van Eyck's *Annunciation*, sadly unavailable for this exhibition, and Memling's *Portrait of a Young Man* (cat. 35a). The former, in which the Archangel Gabriel and the Virgin Mary are depicted on separate panels in grisaille, as if they were painted representations of statues, was acquired in 1933 from a private collection in France, while the latter was another British casualty. It came from the collection of the Duchess of Montrose at Brodick Castle on the Isle of Arran off the west coast of Scotland, and reached the first Baron through the intermediacy of his favourite dealer, Colin Agnew. These extraordinary masterpieces are backed up by a number of other major paintings, and in this field the present Baron has been able to make important additions. They include two panels in the current exhibition, whose authorships are not easily established, but whose quality is not in doubt. In a collection with such exceptional reserves of Renaissance portraits (the first room of the Royal Academy exhibition is given over to them), it is entirely appropriate that they should both be examples of the genre. One is by a Franco-Flemish Master (cat. 33), and the other is attributed to the Master of Flémalle (cat. 32).

If the original emphasis of the collection was on the great masters of the Northern Renaissance, it would nevertheless be wrong to give the impression that the Italians of the same period were totally neglected. On the contrary, five of the rarest and best paintings in the entire collection are Italian works obtained in those *anni mirabili* 1934 and 1935. Sadly, two of them cannot be included in the London exhibition. The first is Domenico Ghirlandaio's ravishing *Portrait of Giovanna Tornabuoni* (fig. 4), which has not left Villa Favorita since 1961, and is well known to be the present Baron's favourite amongst all his beauties. Giovanna was the wife of Lorenzo Tornabuoni, and this portrait, dated 1488, was painted within two years of her marriage on the one hand, and two years of her death on the other. The inscription on the piece of paper behind the figure may be translated as follows: 'If you, o art, could represent also character and virtue, there would be no more beautiful image on the earth.' Giovanna also appears in profile among the bystanders in Domenico's *Visitation*, one of the frescoes he was at work on at this time in the Tornabuoni Chapel in the choir of the Florentine church of Santa Maria Novella.

The second is Carpaccio's imposing *Portrait of a Knight* (fig. 5), dated 1510, which has been convincingly identified as a likeness of Francesco Maria della Rovere, from 1508 Duke of Urbino and from 1523 commander of the Venetian armies. Not only is it the earliest surviving full-length Italian portrait, but it is also one of the supreme achievements of this most irresistible of painters. Both pictures share a common history, having been acquired from prominent American collections, and thus represent very early examples of what might be described as a European backlash. The Ghirlandaio, at one time in the collection of Henry Willet in Brighton, had belonged to the millionaire tycoon J. Pierpont Morgan, and was one of a number of paintings disposed of by the Morgan Library after his death in order to increase their funds for the purchase of books. (The first Baron was also fortunate enough to purchase Fra Angelico's *Madonna and Child* and Jacques Daret's *Nativity* [cat. 16] from the same source at the same time.) At the risk of offending bibliophiles, it might be suggested

5

that the Library made what even it in retrospect would perhaps concede was an error of judgement.

It is an interesting reflection on the history of taste, and on changing standards of sales practice, that when the Carpaccio was in the possession of the Vernon-Wentworth family of Wentworth Castle, Barnsley, Yorkshire, it bore a forged Albrecht Dürer monogram, put on at some unknown date in the past to enhance its value. The London dealer Sully, who sold it in 1919 to Otto H. Kahn, the great patron of the Metropolitan Opera in New York, had the monogram removed. It was not until its restoration in 1958, long after Baron Heinrich's purchase of it, that the true signature and date were rediscovered. By comparison with these two absent giants, Bramantino's *Risen Christ* (cat. 8) and Sebastiano del Piombo's *Ferry Carondolet and His Secretary* (cat. 44) may seem lesser works, but by any normal standard they are nothing of the kind. The Sebastiano again came from a British collection, as indeed did the Bassano *Parable of the Sower* (cat. 5), acquired from the Harewood Collection in 1934. *Ferry Carondolet and His Secretary* was sold by the father of the present Duke of Grafton in 1934 for a few thousand pounds, which must then have seemed a fabulous sum, and certainly did more to keep Euston Hall standing than an old and no doubt dirty painting hanging in a place of no particular honour on the stairs. Neither the fact that the portrait was long attributed to Raphael, nor a provenance stretching back to the great Arundel Collection in the seventeenth century are likely to have been at the forefront of the Duke's mind when he sold it. At the time of all these various pictures' departures abroad, they were each only a few among many.

The final masterpiece acquired in these two years is arguably the most interesting catch of all. Like the Dürer, it came from Palazzo Barberini. Caravaggio's *Saint Catherine of Alexandria* (cat. 10) is one of an ever-dwindling handful of works by the artist still in private hands, and might well be acknowledged to be the finest of them all. Today any private collector or museum would leap at the opportunity of purchasing such a picture, but in the 1930s Italian Baroque paintings and even the works of Caravaggio were out of favour. It showed great presence of mind on the part of the first Baron to choose this particular picture, and in this connection it is worth noting that by 1930 he already owned Valentin's *David with the Head of Goliath* (cat. 50). The collection formed by the first Baron was an outstanding one, and cannot simply be explained as the plaything of a rich man in the right place at the right time. An immense amount of knowledge and especially discernment is required to pick one's way through the attributional minefield of old master paintings connoisseurship, and Baron Heinrich's successes far outweigh any occasional lapses. In this, at least from around 1930, he was certainly aided by the scholarship of Doctor Rudolf Heinemann, who also advised his son, but the taste and character of the collection were his own.

Inevitably, whereas the 1930s were an ideal time for collecting, the war years and their immediate aftermath proved unpropitious, and few works of art were added to the collection before the first Baron's death in 1947. By this date the collection numbered some 525 works and was already an extremely distinguished one, more than able to hold its own with those of European rivals, whether contemporaries such as Calouste Gulbenkian, whose tastes were more catholic but less exquisite, or collectors of a somewhat younger generation such as Count Antoine Seilern and Robert von Hirsch (from whose posthumous sale the present Baron acquired paintings by Luca di Tommé and Bernhard Strigel). Nevertheless, it cannot be claimed that the collection was more remarkable than those of the most illustrious American millionaires to have come under Duveen's wing. What however does distinguish the Thyssen-Bornemisza

Collection from those of Kress, Mellon and even Frick is that it is still in private hands and is still very significantly expanding. Virtually all the great twentieth-century collections have only lasted for a single generation.

At the first Baron's death the old master paintings, the majority of which were already housed in the picture-gallery at Villa Favorita, were not left to the present Baron alone, but to him and his brother and two sisters. Since specific paintings had not been assigned to particular individuals, it was necessary to devise some fair means of dividing them up. Instead of estimating their respective values in monetary terms, which it was thought might involve needless distraction, each picture was given a score. The highest total, not entirely unexpectedly, was awarded to the Ghirlandaio portrait, top with an awesome 450 points. By way of comparison, the magnificent Frans Hals portrait group (fig. 6) was well behind with 300 points.

The present Baron almost immediately decided that he wanted to keep up the collection, and looking at the distinctly bare walls of the gallery at Villa Favorita gave him a simple but at the same time inspired idea. He knew little about pictures, and had never previously been attracted by the idea of collecting— why not begin by buying back as many of his father's pictures from the other members of his family as he could? The process has been a long one, and indeed the Baron's Fra Angelico was re-acquired from his sister as recently as 1986. Another family picture, which reached the collection by an even more circuitous route, was Petrus Christus's *Madonna of the Dry Tree* (cat. 11). It belonged to one of the present Baron's aunts, who promised to leave it to him in her will on account of his passion for art, but then changed her mind. Instead she gave it to the West German Chancellor, Konrad Adenauer. Had it been bequeathed to him, the Baron could never have removed an object of such national importance from West Germany. By great good fortune, however, it subsequently found its way to Switzerland, where he was able to purchase it in 1956, before the death of either Adenauer or his aunt.

The first painting the present Baron bought, as opposed to bought back, was the splendid *Portrait of a Man* (cat. 13) by Francesco del Cossa, which he acquired from the Jan von Pannwitz Collection in 1954. His father had already purchased two small panels of *Saint Clare* and *Saint Catherine* by Cossa from the collection of the Earl of Wemyss at Gosford House in 1935, and a

6

Renaissance portrait was not exactly out of place in the collection. On this evidence taken in isolation, it would have been reasonable to surmise that he was not going to stray far from the strengths of the first Baron's collection. If that was the original intention, however, the intervening decades have witnessed considerable changes.

As has been stated above, the main distinction of Baron Heinrich's collection derived from its northern and to a lesser extent Italian Renaissance paintings, but its range was not rigidly confined to these areas. There were also a few seventeenth-century Dutch flower pieces, genre scenes and landscapes, as well as the occasional eighteenth-century Venetian *veduta*. However, one may suspect that such pictures were little more than wall-fillers of almost unimaginably good quality, for it does not appear to have been the first Baron's intention to widen his range significantly. While the present Baron loves to be surrounded by beautiful pictures, and he has a pair of spectacular Canalettos in the formal dining-room at Villa Favorita, the majority of his acquisitions are intended for the collection.

Arguably the most notable area of expansion has been in the Baroque, with the result that it is possible in the current exhibition to present an outstanding group of paintings by followers of Caravaggio from both north and south of the Alps. The Valentin has already been mentioned, but all the others were acquired in the last ten years or so. The first was Orazio Gentileschi's *Lot and His Daughters* (cat. 21) (1977), followed by Ter Brugghen's *Esau Selling His Birthright* (cat. 48) (1980) and Mattia Preti's *Concert* (cat. 38) (1983). Seen together, they have the distinction of all being decidedly different from one another, and may perhaps provoke one to wonder whether one of the reasons for Caravaggio's unprecedented international influence was not the openness of his revolution. By contrast, the more academic art of the Carracci, which was to have a far more dominating effect on Italian painters of the next generation, is not represented in the exhibition. It hardly features in the collection as a whole. Even Carlo Saraceni, whose exquisite little *Mars and Venus* (cat. 42) on copper, acquired as recently as 1982 from the Suida-Manning Collection in New York, would not lead one to think so, was deeply influenced by Caravaggio.

In general, however, the Baron's tastes tend to involve him in the pursuit of quality rather than in a quest for the works of any one particular artist or school, although there are exceptions to this rule. The Baron's father certainly had favourite artists—Cranach is a case in point, El Greco is another. So it must, for instance, have given the Baron particular pleasure to be able to complement his father's El Grecos by adding the early *Annunciation* (cat. 24) from the Contini-Bonacossi Collection, which he acquired in 1975. Similarly, the first Baron owned a very fine Kalf, which has been joined by two more, including in 1978 the *Still Life with Chinese Porcelain Bowl and Ewer* (cat. 30) from the collection of the Baron's sister Baroness Bentinck-Thyssen. There have also been cases of two pictures by the same artist, previously unrepresented in the collection, being bought in fairly quick succession. Ribera's *Saint Jerome* (1981) and *Pietà* (1985) fall into this category, as do Watteau's *La Halte* (cat. 51) (1975) and *Pierrot content* (cat. 52) (1977), two more pictures which returned to Europe after a stay in America.

In other instances one has the impression that the desire is to buy the perfect example of a given artist's work. Saenredam's *West Façade of the Church of Saint Mary, Utrecht* (cat. 41) which was acquired from Anton Jurgens of Egham in Surrey in 1978, would appear to fit this category. One day it might conceivably be paired with one of the artist's celebrated church interiors.

Any major collector is kept well informed by the great auction houses about their forthcoming attractions, and it goes without saying that dealers are not reticent about offering their treasures either. In this regard, however, the Baron enjoys—if that is the word—a different status from all but a handful of collectors. It would be meaningless to speak of rivals, but Norton Simon is probably the only other individual to compete at this level, while both the J. Paul Getty Museum and the Kimbell Art Museum at Fort Worth are conspicuous and successful buyers at the moment. Sherman Lee of the Cleveland Museum of Art was a man the Baron also greatly respected, but he is now retired, and Cleveland is perhaps no longer quite the force in this respect as it once was.

The consequence of the Baron's reputation as a collector is that every post brings unsolicited photographs or transparencies of pictures being offered for sale by private individuals. Inevitably, most are not even worth looking at, and the labour of doing so is dealt with by the Baron's staff (led, until recently, by Simon de Pury, and now by Irene Martin). If a painting seems to have genuine possibilities, then it is shown to the Baron. He is not a man who likes to seek out advice, but he does have all the resources of a modern museum curator at his disposal, notably an excellent art history library and a conservator (for many years Marco Grassi, and now Emil Bosshard with an up-to-date restoration studio). Years of looking at works of art and living with his collection have given the Baron an 'eye' for pictures, not a gift that is easily acquired, and something by no means all museum people, far less academics, can lay claim to.

The Baron's fortune does however allow him to do some things the rest of us cannot. One of the most commonplace and harmless pastimes of the majority of exhibition-goers must be trying to decide which of the works of art they would most like to take home with them. For the Baron the idea of one day owning almost any object in a private collection may be rather more than an idle fancy, although even he may have to wait his turn. The *Card Players* by Lucas van Leyden (cat. 31), formerly in the collection of Lady Dunsany of Dunsany Castle, County Meath, Ireland, was purchased in 1971. By comparison with some of the grander works in the Thyssen-Bornemisza Collection, it may appear almost modest for all its undoubted charm. But the Baron had long admired it before it became his, having seen it at the *Exhibition of Dutch Art* at the Royal Academy in 1952-1953.

It goes without saying that there have also been the might-have-beens, and the ones that got away. The most notable of these was Leonardo da Vinci's *Portrait of Ginevra de' Benci*. It was the greatest treasure of the Ruling Prince of Lichtenstein, who said he would never be prevailed upon to sell it. Nevertheless the Baron was confident he had first refusal on the painting, and a price had even been agreed. In the end, however, the work was acquired by the National Gallery of Art in Washington for a considerably larger sum, which was for a long time generally thought to have been the record price paid for a painting. Other pictures such as Velazquez's *Juan de Pareja* and Rembrandt's *Aristotle Contemplating the Bust of Homer* were also missed, on both occasions on account of lack of funds at the time.

One consequence of this is a procedure that is quite unexceptional in the case of private collectors, but cannot be deplored too strongly in the case of public institutions, namely de-accessioning. On one particularly memorable occasion, the Baron exchanged a dozen of his own pictures for the unique *bozzetto* (sketch) for Tintoretto's *Paradise* in the Doge's Palace in Venice. The term *bozzetto* hardly does this canvas, which was one of the highlights of the Royal Academy's *Genius of Venice* exhibition in 1983-1984, justice: it is 1.25 metres high by 4.9 metres wide.

It has already been mentioned that the collection was first shown to the public at the Neue Pinakothek in Munich in 1930. A select number of pictures remained in Munich, and were shown at the Alte Pinakothek the next year. Since 1948 the galleries at Castagnola have opened to the public for about half the year, and the present Baron has also proved remarkably generous with loans. Thus, in recent years pictures from the collection have been seen in London at the Royal Academy's *Genius of Venice* exhibition and Matthiesen's 1984 *From Borso to Cesare d'Este, 1450-1628, The School of Ferrara*. Even more significant, however, than loans such as these, have been the exhibitions solely devoted to masterpieces from the collection, of which this is the most recent. In 1961, the National Gallery played host to an 118-picture exhibition of Old Masters, (of the fifty-odd pictures in the current exhibition, however, a staggering twenty have been bought in the intervening years) in the wake of similar shows in Rotterdam (1959-1960) and Essen (1960). Since then, there have been memorable exhibitions in various American museums (1979-1981) and in Paris (1982).

More recently still, there have been exchange exhibitions with the Soviet Union (1983-1987) and Hungary (1985), in which a loan of mutual works from the collection have striven to increase cultural understanding between East and West. In the age of *glasnost*, such exchanges may well increase, and the Baron has been able to talk personally about his hopes with Mrs Gorbachev—she expressed a particular fondness for the Baron's Kalf (cat. 30). As for the future, the Baron will doubtless continue to improve his collection by judicious additions, but it would be a brave man who attempted to guess what might take his fancy next. What is certain is that it is his passionate desire that the Thyssen-Bornemisza Collection should last beyond his own time. To that effect he has set up a foundation to look after the collection and its affairs. Similarly, a new gallery to house the Modern Masters has been designed by the celebrated British architect, James Stirling; if realised, it would be constructed in the grounds of Villa Favorita. What can be stated with considerable confidence is that the collection's like will never be assembled again, not simply because of the unimaginable expense of such an enterprise, but because paintings of this quality are no longer to be found in private hands. What must have seemed an unquenchable stream of masterpieces to the Baron's father is slowly but surely running dry. In its wake the Thyssen-Bornemisza Collection will stand as a monument to the last golden age in the collecting of old master paintings.

David Ekserdjian

CATALOGUE OF WORKS

Note: All paintings are in oil unless otherwise specified.

ALBRECHT ALTDORFER   1. PORTRAIT OF A YOUNG WOMAN

Born 1480, probably in Regensburg
Died 1538 in Regensburg

Deal panel, 59×45.2 cm
Acquired in 1929

Albrecht Altdorfer, together with Albrecht Dürer and Lucas Cranach, was one of the three greatest artists of the German Renaissance. He was a painter and print-maker of distinction who was also, as the town chronicle of his native Regensburg informs us, its municipal architect. Indeed, spectacular buildings are a notable feature of his pictures, as are lush forest landscapes, executed with all the elaboration and romanticism that characterises the Danube School of painting. Equally at home with religious and mythological subject-matter, the principal reason he is not as well known as the other two members of the trio is that the majority of his works has remained in Germany. The great rarity in his corpus are portraits, which makes this splendid panel, probably dating from around 1525-1530, virtually unique. There is one independent male portrait—of a cleric—by Altdorfer, but the only other female portraits are the gaggle of female donors in his splendid *Christ Taking Leave of His Mother* in the National Gallery, London. These hardly compare, however, because they are so small in scale that the artist has not really been able to treat them as individual likenesses.

There is no doubt that this portrait is by Altdorfer: the facial type and expression, the bold colour-scheme, even the distinctively stumpy little thumb all betray his hand. He represents a smartly-dressed young woman three-quarter length, against a rich and variegated green drapery that complements the bright red of her skirt. The same sort of play of colours, albeit subtler, is found in the pale blue-green and salmon pink shot material of her bodice. Her hands, which emerge from billowing spotless white cuffs, are almost weighed down with rings, and she seems to toy with them uncomfortably. Her expression, however, as she looks away to one side, is relaxed. Since there are no other female portraits in Altdorfer's oeuvre, it has been proposed that this may be a representation of his wife, but such a suggestion has more to do with sentimentality than with scholarship. What the picture does demonstrate, on the other hand, is that the scarcity of portraits by Altdorfer has nothing to do with the artist's lack of confidence in this genre.

Born c. 1430 in Messina
Died 1479 in Messina

Panel, 27.5×21 cm
Signed on the stone parapet: 'ANTONELLUS MESSANUS PINX'
Acquired in 1964

Antonello da Messina, as his name implies, was born in Sicily but may well have learnt his art in Naples. He occupies a crucial place in the history of Italian Renaissance painting, mainly by virtue of his activity in Venice in 1475-1476. Like the shadowy figure of Colantonio (cat. 12), who is traditionally supposed to have been his master, he was profoundly influenced by contemporary Netherlandish painting, both in his technique, which involves the use of the oil medium at a very early date, and in his style. This is particularly apparent in two aspects of his work: his landscapes, with their meticulous rendering of detail and their atmospheric treatment of light, and his portraits, of which this is a characteristic example. Both the use of a dark background behind the figure and of a parapet in front, devices designed to concentrate attention on the sitter, are common in the portraits of Jan van Eyck and Rogier van der Weyden. From them too comes the painstaking, almost obsessional attention to detail, which requires that every curl of hair on the man's head and even the stubble of his beard be carefully delineated. Other elements, however, are more personal, with the result that the overall impression is completely different from that of Antonello's Northern prototypes. This is illustrated in the way the sharp lighting of the face is employed to define its structure, and also in the alert, almost amused expression, which the artist strove to capture on more than one occasion.

Although it is closer in mood to the portraits of a year or two before Antonello's trip to Venice, this work has generally been dated to the Venetian period. The panel has been cut at the bottom, and in consequence the signature, 'ANTONELLUS MESSANUS PINX' (pinxit = painted) has been truncated. It was the clarity, directness and precision of portraits such as this that were to influence Antonello's contemporary, Giovanni Bellini, and ultimately even those giants of the next generation in Venice, Giorgione and Titian.

HANS BALDUNG
(called Grien)

3. PORTRAIT OF A LADY

Born 1484 or 1485 in Schwabisch
Gmüd
Died 1545 in Strasburg

Deal panel, 68×51.5 cm
Signed and dated at the upper left: 'HB 1530'
Acquired in 1934

This portrait is inscribed with the letters 'HB' and the date '1530' in the top left hand corner. Were it not for this fact, it can safely be said that it would not have been associated with the name of the distinguished German Renaissance painter, Hans Baldung. Indeed, before the uncovering of the monogram and the date it was not unreasonably connected with Lucas Cranach the Elder. This is not simply a matter of one artist being influenced by the manner of another, but rather an instance of one picture being directly dependent on another. Baldung's source would appear to have been a *Salome* by Cranach now in the Szepmüveszeti Muzeum in Budapest, or if not a closely related variant. In such pictures, whether representing Salome or Judith, Cranach adopted a formula in which the figure is decked out in contemporary finery and confronts our gaze with an alert look that borders on the menacing. Baldung has adopted all these aspects of his source, and transformed the depiction of the Biblical heroine into a portrait by the simple expedient of leaving out her attributes. The result is an elegant and stylish image of a young woman with strings of pearls in her immaculately coiffed hair, feathers in her broad-brimmed hat, jewels at her neck and on her hand—all in all a perfectly fashionable harmony of green, red and golden orange. Even her face conforms to an ideal, not admittedly one in accordance with classical canons of beauty, but an ideal nonetheless, as countless thin-eyed, sharp-featured and pale complexioned Cranach ladies amply testify. The painting was for a long time considered to be the wedding portrait of a Baden-Durlach princess, but this is not possible on historical grounds. What is more, one may legitimately wonder if it was even intended to be a likeness of any real woman, as opposed to an image of a beauty designed for the delectation of a patron, who cared not at all whether such a creature existed anywhere other than in the mind of the artist and on his panel.

FRA BARTOLOMMEO
(Baccio della Porta)

4. NATIVITY WITH THE YOUNG SAINT JOHN THE BAPTIST

Born 1472 in Florence
Died 1517 in Pian di Mugnone

Poplar panel, 62×47 cm
Acquired in 1955

In the Renaissance, it was popularly believed that Christ and Saint John the Baptist first met not—as a reading of the Gospels would suggest—at the Baptism of Christ, but rather during their childhood. In art the encounter was either depicted as taking place at the time of the Nativity or on the Holy Family's Flight into Egypt. In this panel by Fra Bartolommeo the presence of three angels above, linking hands to dance a joyous measure and sing glory to God in the highest, not to mention the inclusion of the ox and the ass, as well as the background detail of the shepherds tending their flocks, all demonstrate that the artist has chosen to paint a Nativity. The setting is not a realistic stable, however, but rather the remains of a ruined classical building, in accordance with another well-worn tradition, which associated the coming of Christ with the downfall of the pagan order epitomised by the Roman Empire. The infant Baptist enters tentatively, his arms folded across his breast, and his habitual attributes, the reed cross and scroll, discarded at his feet. The Virgin kneels humbly before her Son, and tenderly presents John, who walks on the hem of her blue robe. In the centre the Christ Child, also on His mother's robe, sits with His legs unsteadily crossed and His head propped up on a bundle, of exactly the kind Saint Joseph carries on the Flight into Egypt. He stretches out His arms eagerly to greet His cousin. Behind Him, the figure of Saint Joseph, beardless as he so often is in the work of Fra Bartolommeo, raises his right hand, perhaps in recognition, and holds his usual attribute, a plain wooden staff, in his left.

The simple, frieze-like composition executed in muted reds, greens, oranges and blues across the entire foreground is remarkable for its tranquillity and order, and is perfectly balanced by the incredible depth of the Northern-inspired landscape with its glorious hazy blue mountainous distance. Although the natural world is idealised, its importance here reminds us that Fra Bartolommeo was a prolific and intensely observant landscape draughtsman at a date when the practice was by no means commonplace. Fra Bartolommeo, whose lay name was Baccio della Porta, was a painter who became a Dominican friar under the influence of the charismatic Prior of San Marco, Girolamo Savonarola. After an interval of a few years he resumed his artistic career while remaining a friar and had a profound effect on his younger contemporary Raphael. Given that Raphael treated the same theme so similarly in a drawing executed some years later, and now in the Ashmolean Museum, Oxford, it is tempting to suppose that he had not forgotten this early work by Fra Bartolommeo, which he might well have admired during his Florentine years.

JACOPO BASSANO
(Jacopo da Ponte)

5. THE PARABLE OF THE SOWER

Born c. 1515 in Bassano
Died 1592 in Bassano

Canvas, 139 × 129 cm
Acquired in 1934

Although Jacopo da Ponte belongs firmly to the Venetian School of painters, he spent most of his working life in his home town, Bassano, from which he took the name by which he is best known. His father, Francesco da Ponte, was a decidedly unremarkable provincial painter, so it was to Venice that Jacopo went to learn his craft. There he joined the workshop of a painter of the second rank, Bonifazio de' Pitati, but from the first he was deeply impressed by the work of Titian, whose influence manifested itself not only in a general stylistic dependence, but also in more specific quotations. From the outset of his career Jacopo was unusually interested in the depiction of landscape, and around 1560 he began to paint a novel kind of picture in which religious subject-matter became subordinated to the overall pastoral effect. Thus, while this canvas has no doubt correctly been identified as a representation of the *Parable of the Sower*—the fowls (shown by Bassano as swallows) devouring the seeds that fell by the wayside seem particularly decisive—it is not entirely surprising that the subject was only recognised as recently as thirty years ago.

The sower of the thirteenth chapter of the Gospel According to Saint Matthew is to the side and occupies the middle ground; he is, in fact, the most distant figure in the entire composition. In contrast to his isolation, the foreground is filled with just the kind of seemingly haphazard group of people and animals that Bassano loved to paint. In the corner a kneeling figure showing her back to us, one of countless variations on this theme in the artist's work, spreads out a simple meal on a plain cloth in preparation for a modest *Déjeuner sur l'herbe*. Behind a young girl gives the sheep something to drink out of a basin, while beyond a boy strains at a pair of distinctly sedentary oxen who are meant to be pulling a plough. Finally, a mother, again shown from behind, looks on, while her son peers down curiously at a snugly curled-up dog. This dog, which ultimately derives from the one on the bed in Titian's so-called *Venus of Urbino* (Uffizi, Florence) was a great favourite with Jacopo, and appears in more than half a dozen of his pictures.

No doubt a drawing of the dog was kept in the workshop, and indeed for all the sensitivity and atmosphere of the landscape here, it should not be forgotten that the picture as a whole is an invention. The various figures derive from Bassano's presumably extensive stock of preliminary drawings, and are grafted onto a largely imaginary setting, which is nevertheless based on the observation of nature. The composition is crowded over to the left, and forms are deliberately cropped at the edge of the picture, while the landscape recedes diagonally to the right until it reaches the sower, only to turn leftwards again into the distance. The brown of the foliage would originally have been green, and has changed colour with age. However, the muted colours of the drapery and the repetition of the blues of the mountains and the sky in the costumes ensure that there is a sense of harmony between the foreground and the background, and likewise between the figures and the landscape.

PSEUDO-BOCCACCINO
(Giovanni Agostino da Lodi)

6a. EPISODE FROM THE STORY OF SYRINX
(Left-hand panel)

Active end of fifteenth century
and beginning of sixteenth century

Poplar panel, 46×36.5 cm
Acquired before 1930

Neither the authorship nor the subject-matter of these two intriguing panels (6a and 6b) is unproblematic. Their painter is generally known as the Pseudo-Boccaccino, because one of his most important surviving works, dated 1500 but not signed, was once attributed to Boccaccio Boccaccino of Cremona. When it was realised that there were two different artists involved, our painter was dubbed the Pseudo-Boccaccino. Subsequently, it was suggested that the Pseudo-Boccaccino and a named artist, Giovanni Agostino da Lodi, were one and the same person, and this idea has gained widespread if not universal acceptance. Certainly the style of the Pseudo-Boccaccino indicated a Lombard origin (Lodi is not far from Milan) around the end of the fifteenth century, not least in a predictable if never slavish debt to Leonardo da Vinci.

The subject-matter of the panels has, no doubt correctly, been thought to be drawn from Ovid's *Metamorphoses*, a favourite source for mythological stories in the Renaissance. However, the specific subjects represented are less easily identified. Artists, who by no means always read Latin with ease, habitually had recourse to Italian translations of Ovid. Such translations were not invariably completely accurate, which may in part explain why these narratives appear to be such free adaptations of Ovid's poem. In the first panel (cat. 6a), Pan, who is shown as half-man, half-beast, attempts to win the heart of Syrinx, a nymph who seems closer to succumbing than Ovid's text would have us suppose. In the middle ground a young man pursues a fleeing girl—they have been called Apollo and Daphne, although neither has any of the relevant attributes. In the other panel (cat. 6b) Syrinx is transformed into reeds to save her from Pan's advances, but there is no sign of him. The river in the foreground represents her father Ladon, to whom she ran for help, but it is hard to believe that he is also meant to be the young man in fashionable attire who tries to embrace her, as has been suggested. This is not the way river-gods were portrayed in the Renaissance, and they were certainly never shown wearing swords. In the middle distance two men in antique dress converse with a bare-breasted woman holding a spear and beyond them are two soldiers, but their identity is again obscure.

Both panels must originally have formed part of a piece of furniture, and would probably have been accompanied by other scenes. They may for instance have been the ends of a wedding chest, or *cassone*. Their great charm lies in the way they allow the landscape to dominate the figures to an extent that would have been unimaginable in the more formal context of a large-scale fresco or altarpiece.

PSEUDO-BOCCACCINO
(Giovanni Agostino da Lodi)

6b. EPISODE FROM THE STORY OF SYRINX
(Right-hand panel)

Active end of fifteenth century
and beginning of sixteenth century

Poplar panel, 46×36.5 cm
Acquired before 1930

(For catalogue note see cat. 6a)

FRANÇOIS BOUCHER
7. LA TOILETTE

Born 1703 in Paris
Died 1770 in Paris

Canvas, 52.5×66.5 cm
Signed and dated at the lower left: 'F. Boucher 1742'
Acquired in 1967

Boucher was a master of the elegant and intimate domestic scene, and this canvas is an exceptionally charming example of the genre. It is signed and dated 1742 in the bottom left-hand corner, and was acquired directly from the artist by Count Karl Gustav Tessin, one of the most notable patrons of French art of the period. Tessin was Swedish Ambassador to the court of King Louis XV from 1735 until 1742, but remained in touch with Boucher after his return to Stockholm. We know that although he sold some of his pictures before his death, *La Toilette* was one of the works with which he did not part.

It has been suggested that this picture represents Mme Boucher, but in fact there are a number of objections to such a view. The first is that the artist is unlikely to have used his wife as a model for such an improper pose. The second is that the features of the woman in the painting are those of a pert and provocative ideal, and have little to do with the far more characterful expression of the girl who posed for the preparatory drawing (now in the Musée des Beaux-Arts, Orléans). The third is that there is a picture by Boucher that has a much better claim to be a likeness of Mme Boucher (Frick Collection, New York), and which clearly represents a different sitter. The woman here is caught tying up her garter, her right leg is stylishly extended, and her left leg splayed to reveal a great expanse of white petticoat beneath which a gleeful cat is playing with a ball of thread. By modern standards the lady's *déshabillé* may seem distinctly modest, but it is worth recalling that she wears nothing under her petticoats, and that the cat's position therefore suggests distinct erotic possibilities, of exactly the kind Fragonard so wittily exploited in his *The Swing* (Wallace Collection, London). The lady turns her gaze to look at a white cap with a red ribbon which her maid holds up for her approval, while all around the paraphernalia of her boudoir distract and enchant the eye. A small screen stands before the blazing fire, and various bits and pieces, including a lit candle and what appears to be another garter, clutter up the mantlepiece. A curl of steam issues invitingly from the dainty little teapot at her side. Behind the two women the background is dominated by a gorgeous yellow Chinese screen adorned with exotic birds, which also appears in the *Portrait of Mme Boucher* referred to above, and half-conceals, half-reveals a delicate pastel portrait, presumably of the lady herself. Finally, over to the right a splendid scarlet garment, edged with fur, has been dumped untidily on the nearest chair. Everything seems to warn that this little lady, so beautiful in her silvery-blue attire, would prove more trouble than she is worth. Yet it is a mark of Boucher's genius that he at the same time makes it well-nigh impossible to resist her appeal.

BRAMANTINO
(Bartolomeo Suardi)

8. THE RISEN CHRIST

Born c. 1465 probably in Milan
Died 1530 in Milan

Poplar panel transferred to masonite panel, 109×73 cm
Acquired in 1934

This haunting picture depicts the Risen Christ: He is represented in three-quarter length showing off the mark of the nail in His right hand, and pointing towards the wound in His side with His left. A bleak stretch of landscape leads back to a full moon, clearly if fancifully adorned with the features of the Man in the Moon. It casts an unearthly light over the scene, and accentuates the contrast between the ghostly pallor of the Redeemer's flesh and the livid red of His blood and hair. The rocky setting to the right suggests the sepulchres in the Garden of Gethsemane, but any potentially distracting accessories attendant on the Resurrection, such as the tomb itself or the Roman soldiers who stood guard over it, have deliberately been excluded. Partially swathed in His white winding-sheet, Christ stands before us, His head tilted slightly to one side, and forces us to return His gaze. His eyes are red with tears, and one look at the intense pathos of His expression is sufficient to convince us that He does not come in triumph.

In the past this work was attributed to Bramante, whose real distinction was as an architect, and compared with his *Christ at the Column* in the Brera, Milan. Now, however, it is generally agreed to be the work of Bartolomeo Suardi, called Bramantino, who was better known than Bramante as a painter, and worked in a similar idiom. The diminutive 'ino' suggests a mere follower, but in fact Bramantino was a highly original, even eccentric artist, who has the distinction of having been almost the only Milanese painter of his generation to emerge unscathed from the influence of Leonardo da Vinci's two sojourns in the city. Little is known of his life, but his is a unique talent, and this awesome painting reveals him at his commanding best.

CANALETTO
(Antonio Canal)

9. WARWICK CASTLE FROM THE SOUTH

Born 1697 in Venice
Died 1768 in Venice

Canvas, 75×120.5 cm
Acquired in 1978

Antonio Canal, called Canaletto, is universally acknowledged to have been the greatest of all the Venetian *vedutisti*, or view-painters, of the eighteenth century. Canaletto appears to have visited England twice, first from 1746 to 1750, and then from mid-1751 to either 1755 or 1756. The majority of his patrons were Englishmen by this date, and he was doubtless encouraged to make the journey by his friend and protector, Joseph Smith, His Majesty's Consul in Venice. During all his years in England Francis Greville, Lord Brooke, later the Earl of Warwick, was one of Canaletto's most faithful patrons, commissioning a total of five paintings of Warwick Castle from him. This one, which can be associated with payments to the artist by Hoare's Bank on Lord Brooke's account dating from 1752, shows the south front of the Castle.

In 1748 Canaletto had already produced a smaller canvas, now in a Private Collection, of the same view, albeit from further away and from a fractionally different angle. In the following year, Lancelot 'Capability' Brown carried out various improvements to the Castle grounds which appear to have been incorporated in Canaletto's version of 1752. The earlier version recorded the presence of an old mill at the foot of the tower to the right, and houses at the end of the bridge. These had presumably been swept away by 'Capability' Brown, who certainly added new planting in the form of trees at the water's edge in front of the Castle, and on Ethelfleda's Mount to the left. Given that the later version also adapts a closer viewpoint, a considerable amount of incidental detail has been eliminated at the edges of the composition, thus increasing the degree to which the Castle itself now comes to dominate its surroundings. A few fashionably dressed figures stroll, chat, or discuss the prospect as if inviting the spectator to associate with the subject of their own contemplation. The small figure fishing adds a poetic mood suggesting man in harmony with nature, while the inclusion of a gilded and canopied barge on the water can hardly fail to remind one of Canaletto's native Venice. Indeed, the warm light that pervades the entire scene, even though the sky is not a cloudless and uniform blue, also seems quintessentially Venetian. Not all his contemporaries admired Canaletto's English pictures, and the diarist George Vertue even recorded the rumour, which he subsequently corrected, that 'he is not the veritable Cannelleti of Venice'. In spite of these doubts, however, the series of pictures of Warwick Castle, of which this is such a distinguished example, is uniquely fascinating for its classical, southern vision of Gothic, northern architecture, and ranks among Canaletto's finest accomplishments.

CANALETTO
(Antonio Canal)

CARAVAGGIO
(Michelangelo Merisi)

10. SAINT CATHERINE OF ALEXANDRIA

Born 1571, probably in Milan
Died 1610 in Porto Ercole

Canvas, 173×133 cm
Acquired in 1935

Saint Catherine of Alexandria was a young lady of noble birth (in some accounts of royal blood), who steadfastly refused to renounce her religion in spite of the brutality of the endeavours of the Emperor Maxentius to make her do so. After persuasion, in the form of fifty learned philosophers whom she worsted in argument, had failed, he had her tied to a spiked wheel. However, before it could do her any harm, it was destroyed by celestial intervention. Finally, he had her beheaded, at which point angels descended from heaven and transported her body to Mount Sinai for burial.

In this imposing canvas Caravaggio shows Saint Catherine surrounded by various of her attributes, caught in a moment beyond time. The broken wheel (the Catherine Wheel) is by her side, and she toys with the sword of her execution, kneeling on a splendid red cushion as if waiting for the end. Yet this is no narrative, as the presence of the extremely prominent palm of martyrdom in the foreground is intended to remind us.

Caravaggio's canvas has rightly been seen as a work of transition, the first of his large-scale religious pictures after an early career principally devoted to low life and genre scenes of a markedly erotic character. It was painted for the artist's first great patron, Cardinal Francesco del Monte, and was probably executed in the last years of the sixteenth century, just before the decoration of the Contarelli Chapel in the Church of San Luigi dei Francesi in Rome. Both the sharpness of the lighting, here rather unusually coming from the right, and the extraordinary conviction of the rendering of different surfaces and substances are aspects of Caravaggio's revolutionary realism, but his approach to the human figure is at least as significant and influential. Saint Catherine is a beautiful young girl, but she is drawn from the life, not from the artist's imagination, and indeed also appears in at least one other picture by him, the *Conversion of the Magdalen* (Institute of Arts, Detroit). She looks out at us, and for all the distractions of her attributes and her drapery, which is painted with remarkable virtuosity, it is to her that we return. Caravaggio is not yet entirely happy with the full-length format, and tilts the floor slightly alarmingly upwards, but on the whole the picture is a considerable triumph. At an earlier age its sheer size would have suggested that this canvas was intended for an altar in a church, but Cardinal del Monte may well simply have wanted to see what Caravaggio could achieve, and in any event this is surely a private as opposed to a public picture. Looking at the loving way that every minute detail of the proto-rapier is delineated with almost scientific accuracy, one cannot help recalling that Caravaggio was something of an expert on swords: he used one to kill Ranuccio Tommasoni on 29 May 1606 after an argument over a bet of 10 *scudi* on a game of tennis.

CARAVAGGIO

Born c. 1410 in Baerle, Brabant
Died 1472 or 1473 in Bruges

Oak panel, 14.7×12.4 cm
Acquired in 1965

Petrus Christus, as well as being the most faithful follower of Jan van Eyck, was a highly gifted artist in his own right. This little picture, executed in oil on oak panel with all the delicacy of touch of a miniature, is an unusually fascinating and pleasing example of his work. It would appear to date from the early part of his career, and is very close in style to the *Madonna and Child with Saint Barbara presenting Jan de Vos*, also known as the 'Exeter Madonna' (Gemäldegalerie, Berlin-Dahlem).

At a date shortly before 1463, Petrus Christus and his wife were recorded as members of a Bruges confraternity, 'Onze Lieve Vrauwe ten Drooghen Boome' (Our Lady of the Dry Tree), a religious brotherhood with a particular veneration for the Immaculate Conception. It drew many of its members from the highest nobility on the one hand, and senior ecclesiastics on the other, but there was also room for the humble painter. Members of the Confraternity were expected to do good works, and around their necks they wore medals of gold or silver, whose iconography corresponded with that of Petrus's picture. No doubt both were based on a larger cult image, perhaps housed in the choir chapel of the Franciscan church in Bruges where the confraternity worshipped.

In this work the Virgin and Child are shown surrounded by the angular branches of the Dry Tree, which act as a sort of *mandorla* around them, and at the same time bear a striking resemblance to Christ's Crown of Thorns. From the lifeless branches of the tree there hang fifteen golden Gothic letter A's, each one symbolising one of the Ave Marias of the 'Hail Mary'. The Child, who holds the fruit of Adam and Eve's sin in his left hand, is half-clothed rather than—as was more common by this date—naked. The Virgin, who is clad in a red robe lined with green and a blue dress edged with ermine, is a strikingly unaffected figure, with her free-flowing hair and her wonderfully natural expression.

Given the artist's connection with the Confraternity, it is extremely likely that this most private of pictures was executed for someone he knew personally. Interestingly enough, the iconography of the Dry Tree is so unusual that a legend sprang up to explain it. It was claimed that Philip the Good, Duke of Burgundy, founded the Confraternity after his prayers before an image of the Virgin and Child stuck between the branches of a barren tree, which he came upon in the midst of battle against the French, were answered and defeat was turned into victory. Sadly, there is evidence that the Confraternity was already in existence in 1396, the year of Philip's birth.

COLANTONIO
(Niccolò Antonio)
(attributed to)

12. THE CRUCIFIXION

Active in Naples from c. 1420
to c. 1460

Panel, 33×44 cm
Acquired in 1976

In spite of its outstandingly high quality and exceptional historical interest, it is by no means easy to establish the authorship or even the nationality of this fascinating picture. For while there is general agreement concerning its debt to the work of Jan van Eyck, it is clearly not by a Netherlandish artist. It has been suggested that it may be Spanish, but it seems more likely that it is Italian and was executed in Naples. We know that an important painter called Colantonio (short for Niccolò Antonio) was the leading figure at the court of King René of Anjou at Naples. Furthermore, we are informed that Colantonio was the master of Antonello da Messina. The dependence of this picture on an Eyckian model, whether a panel painting or a manuscript illumination, can scarcely be doubted, and the same is true of its importance for Antonello, to whom one recent critic has gone so far as to attribute it. However, these factors do not of themselves make its connection with Colantonio incontrovertible. The main objection to his authorship, in fact, may be that it is too good; it certainly looks much more advanced than his only really secure works, *Saint Jerome in His Study* (Museo di Capodimonte, Naples), and the *Saint Vincent Ferrer Altarpiece* (San Pietro Martire, Naples).

In the centre of the composition the figure of Christ is treated with brutal realism. His eyes are open in death, His face already coloured a livid blue-grey, and dried streams of blood have poured from His wounds and stained His loincloth. On either side of Him the two thieves are bound rather than nailed to their crosses, and their characters are cleverly differentiated: the good one on His right bows his head in resigned if agonised acceptance of his fate, while on His left—or sinister—side, the bad thief, whose right leg has broken free from his bonds, raises his head for a last scream of pain. Below them a substantial crowd has gathered, mostly comprising soldiery in distinctly oriental uniforms and Jews, with the holy personages in the centre. The Virgin, who is only just visible, has fainted, and her body is being supported by one of the Holy Women, while the grieving Saint John the Evangelist, the disciple Christ loved and commanded to look after His mother, cups her head in his hands. The third woman faces us with arms outstretched and wails a lamentation: she is Veronica, with her attribute, the *sudarium* (the veil on which the face of Christ was imprinted when she wiped away His sweat on the Road to Calvary). Behind this group, the solitary figure of Mary Magdalen stands wrapt in awe at the foot of the cross. In the ranks of the onlookers a whole range of emotions, from indifference to wonderment, is conveyed. The skull reminds us that Calvary was also called Golgotha—the place of a skull—according to Matthew, Mark, and John. Down below, in the distance, is the City of Jerusalem, and not far to its right a detail that seems to betray the artist's awareness of northern art, namely a windmill. The large disc in the sky archaically rendered in silver over gold leaf is meant to represent the moon, a reference to the fact that 'when the sixth hour was come, there was darkness over the whole land until the ninth hour'.

Born 1436 in Ferrara
Died 1478 in Bologna

Poplar panel, 38.3×27.3 cm
Acquired in 1954

In Italy, in the first half of the fifteenth century, it was customary for portraits to represent their sitters in profile, often against a plain background. In the second half of the century the idea of showing the sitter looking straight out of the picture became popular, and a background depicting the world beyond was also often introduced. In this portrait the young man confronts our gaze with unusual directness, and particular emphasis is laid upon the ring which he holds in his left hand. Not only does the hand overstep the barrier of the parapet, which in most such portraits would serve to divide his world from ours, but in addition his sleeve casts a very palpable shadow upon it.

The prominence of the ring and the intensity of the gaze suggested a neat solution to early scholars, namely that this was a self-portrait of the Bolognese goldsmith and painter Francesco Francia, an identification supported by a seventeenth-century engraving after the picture. More recently, the portrait has been attributed on grounds of style to another artist working in Bologna, the Ferrarese painter Francesco del Cossa. Since Cossa was in Bologna from 1472 it has been suggested that the sitter could still be Francia. However, a sitter holding a ring need not necessarily be a goldsmith by trade. Rather, such a representation was frequently used at the time to demonstrate that the sitter had recently become betrothed. While the identification of the sitter may ultimately remain unresolved, the style of this portrait places it within the final period of Cossa's career.

The evidence for this proposed dating lies mostly in the confidence of the rendering of forms, especially of the hand, and in the treatment of the landscape, both of which are eminently comparable with the *Saint Vincent Ferrer* of much the same date in the National Gallery, London. The origins of this kind of geological setting, with its eccentric rock formations and grey-brown colours, go back to Mantegna, but Cossa gives it a character that is uniquely his. The barren trees against the sky, and a few anecdotal details—a man fishing, a galleon, a distant town at the foot of ice-blue mountains—do little to relieve the general atmosphere of bleakness. Yet it would be wrong to exaggerate the severity of this portrait, and it is worth recalling that Cossa was also responsible for some of the most joyous scenes in all fifteenth-century art in the frescoes of the Palazzo Schifanoia in Ferrara.

14. HERCULES AT THE COURT OF OMPHALE

Born 1510 in Wittenberg
Died 1537 in Bologna

Beech panel, 57.7×85 cm
Signed at the right centre with the monogram 'HC' around a winged dragon (the Cranach heraldic symbol) and dated '1537'
Acquired before 1930

A number of very similar treatments of this subject by the artist's famous father, Lucas Cranach the Elder, are known, and were it not for the 'HC' and serpent monogram at the centre of the right edge of the panel, this painting would have been attributed to father rather than son. In fact it is one of only two known signed works by Hans (the other, a portrait, is also in the Thyssen-Bornemisza Collection), who died young and appears to have worked exclusively in his father's style, albeit with considerable skill.

The painting represents the episode in the life of Hercules when, having killed his friend Phitus in a fit of madness, he was punished by being sold as a slave to Omphale, the Queen of Lydia, for three years. Although they became lovers, she added to his subjugation by decking him out in women's clothes and making him spin yarn. Cranach shows Hercules sitting in the centre of the composition, hard at work, and surrounded by attractive, partially veiled young women who amuse themselves by pulling some sort of a kerchief over his head and by presenting him with the tools of his new trade. He sports slashed black breeches and a fine cod-piece. The inscription, a Latin quatrain inspired by Ovid, which is also found in his father's representations of the subject, may be translated as follows: 'To the hands of Hercules the maidens of Lydia gave work—The Divine is subjected to the rule of his lady—Thus ruinous pleasure grasps hold of great spirits—And even the ablest souls are wearied by gentle love.' The text may be intended to point a high moral, but the picture itself is a bantering comedy concerned with the domination of man by woman in a world turned upside down. The fact that the figures, not least the girls, are dressed in the height of fashion with no attempt at ancient costume must presumably have given the satire added bite. Normally in paintings of this subject Omphale is shown wearing Hercules's lion-skin and brandishing his club, but here none of the girls is so dressed nor in any way differentiated from her fellows. Instead Omphale is not included, and it follows that we, as spectators, are being cast in the role of the triumphant Queen of Lydia, lording it over the anxious-looking hero. Against the green background wall behind the figures, there hangs a meticulous still-life of two dead birds, of a kind that seems to have been invented by Jacopo de' Barbari, an Italian painter and print-maker who spent much of his influential career in Germany. Although Hans Cranach died in Bologna and this picture is dated to the last year of his life, it is unlikely to have been executed in Italy, because the support—a beech panel—is a typically Northern one.

Born 1620 at Dordrecht
Died 1691 at Dordrecht

Oak Panel, 47×71 cm
Acquired in 1957

Aelbert Cuyp was a pupil of his father, Jacob Gerritsz. Cuyp, who was particularly renowned as a painter of portraits in his native Dordrecht. Initially, Aelbert followed in his father's footsteps, but soon widened his range and became proficient in a variety of genres. It is for his landscapes, however, that he is justly most famous. Early in his career he was considerably influenced by the landscapes of Salomon van Ruysdael, and then in the paintings of his maturity he almost approaches Claude Lorrain, an artist he could have been acquainted with through Jan Both, who had studied with Claude in Rome. This exquisite panel is a fine example of Cuyp at his best, with the landscape bathed in a positively Italianate glow, worlds away from the more sombre achievements of the majority of his Dutch contemporaries. The foreground of the picture, with its low-lying foliage and dirty farm track, acts as an introduction to the muted action of the middle-ground. There, in the very centre of the image, is the solitary figure of a cowherd, his white shirt caught by the rays of the evening sun, his stick resting on his shoulder. It is not by chance that we cannot see his face as he guides his few brown and white cows over a ramshackle wooden bridge to the right. The bridge runs over a river or stream, whose destination is the lake to the left, a flat expanse of water fringed by trees, to which the eye is irresistibly drawn. The only prominent trees are those to the right, which divide the skyline into two uneven halves and stand out against the rocky escarpment. The detailed observation on earth seems to give way to freer effects in the sky, with birds silhouetted against the grey clouds tinged with white and against the pinkish yellow tones of the setting sun. Cuyp does not appear to have felt the need to leave his native Dordrecht, and it is known that he married well and held various public offices there. It is certainly not hard to believe that this golden evocation of the countryside was created by a man at peace with the world.

16. THE NATIVITY

Active between 1418 and 1468

Oak panel, 60×53 cm
Acquired in 1935

This panel, together with others representing the *Visitation*, the *Adoration of the Magi* (both Gemäldegalerie, Berlin-Dahlem), and the *Presentation of Christ in the Temple* (Musée du Petit Palais, Paris), originally formed the side wings of an altarpiece which the Benedictine Abbot of Sant Vaast, Jean du Clercq, commissioned from Jacques Daret in 1433 and completed two years later. The central part of the complex contained a sculptured group of the *Coronation of the Virgin*, while below were alabaster statues of the twelve apostles.

Daret, whose only securely attributed works these are, was profoundly influenced by his teacher, Robert Campin (cat. 32), and in particular by his masterly *Nativity*, now in the Musée des Beaux-Arts at Dijon. This is true both formally and iconographically, although the embellishments to the bare bones of the gospel story are not absolutely identical in the two treatments. In the Apocryphal Gospels of Pseudo-James and Pseudo-Matthew, it is recorded that two midwives were present at the Birth of Christ. One of them, originally called Zelomi, but subsequently Zebel or even Rachel, believed in Mary's virginity, while the other, Salome, demanded tangible proof. Her lack of faith was rewarded by the withering of her hand which was only made whole after she had touched the new-born Saviour. In Campin's picture the doubting midwife is told what to do by an angel while her companion looks on in wonder, whereas in Daret's composition she is instructed by her companion. Another legend is alluded to by Joseph's holding a candle: the vision of the Nativity enjoyed by the mystic Saint Bridget of Sweden included a description of light so bright that it outshone Joseph's candle. Here, although the scene is set in broad daylight rather than at night, this symbolic particular is recalled and a golden radiance issues forth from the Child lying naked on the ground as if in answer to the one above the stable. One major difference between this version and its model is that in the latter the shepherds have just arrived at the stable, whereas Daret includes them in a background vignette, hearing the tidings of great joy from an angel carrying a fluttering scroll. A goldfinch, one of the most common symbols of the Passion, is perched on the stable roof, where icicles remind us of the season. The fashionable elegance of the midwives, with their brocaded and fur-trimmed costumes, is combined with an attractive naïvety, evident in both the facial expressions of the human participants, and the humble ox and ass who join them in adoration. Daret may not be an artist of the stature of his master, Robert Campin, or his fellow-apprentice Rogier van der Weyden (cat. 53), but he remains one of the most enchanting of all the early Netherlandish painters.

DOSSO DOSSI
(Giovanni Luteri)

17. THE MARTYRDOM OF SAINT STEPHEN

Documented 1512 in Mantua
Died 1542 in Ferrara

Canvas, 80×90 cm
Acquired in 1977

Dosso Dossi was the foremost member of the extremely gifted and highly original school of painters active in Ferrara in the first half of the sixteenth century. His less talented younger brother, Battista Dossi, worked in a similar style, and since the two are known to have collaborated, it is not always easy to attribute individual paintings to one of them rather than the other. A canvas of this scale, however, is not likely to have involved both brothers, and its high quality suggests it is by Dosso rather than Battista.

The subject is the stoning of Saint Stephen, the first Christian martyr, as it is recounted in the seventh chapter of the Acts of the Apostles. Stephen, who was also one of the seven 'men of honest report' appointed a deacon by the twelve disciples, is tonsured and clad accordingly. He kneels barefoot on the ground, his hands joined in prayer on the model of a Christ in the Agony in the Garden. He is perhaps to be imagined looking up 'steadfastly into heaven' towards the radiance in the top lefthand corner of the picture and seeing 'the glory of God, and Jesus standing on the right hand of God'. His equally brightly-clad executioners are in contemporary costume, of a kind worn by German mercenaries, or Landsknechts. They form a ring around him, which is completed by the figure of a young man, almost a boy, seated on the ground and seen from behind. He is Saul, at whose feet we are told, 'the witnesses laid down their clothes'. The narrative occupies the foreground, while in the world beyond life goes on as normal, with figures sitting in a rowing boat and walking along a coastal path completely unaware of the drama that is unfolding not all that far away.

The Ferrarese in general, and Dosso in particular, are noted for their interest in landscape, which is amply testified by the splendid background here. Luxurious greens are played off against atmospheric blues, in the midst of which is Dosso's vision of the city of Jerusalem. For many Renaissance artists its portrayal offered an ideal opportunity for a display of classical erudition, but in Dosso's hands it becomes a Northern-inspired fantasy of turrets and pinnacles in the lea of a romantic foliage-haunted mountain. The relatively small scale of the picture, and the limited amount of the composition given over to the figures both suggest that it was painted with a private destination in mind, and this may also explain the prominence given to the landscape.

DUCCIO
DI BUONINSEGNA

18. CHRIST AND THE WOMAN OF SAMARIA

First documented 1278 in Siena
Died 1319 in Siena

Panel with gold background, 43.5×46 cm
Acquired in 1971

Duccio's *Maestà* ('Madonna in Majesty') originally adorned the high altar of the Cathedral of his home town, Siena. Completed in 1311, and carried in procession through the streets of the city in triumph, it was the artist's crowning achievement and is the supreme masterpiece of fourteenth-century panel painting in Italy. An immense double-sided altarpiece of unprecedented splendour and complexity, its front depicted Siena's patron saint, the Virgin Mary, enthroned as Queen of Heaven and surrounded by saints and angels. In the predella at the foot of the main panel were small panels showing scenes from the early life of Christ, and above it stories of the Virgin's death and assumption. The back panel carried an elaborate narrative sequence leading from Christ's temptation and miracles in the predella through the events of the passion in the main panel, and culminating with Christ's appearances after the resurrection, and the Pentecost, at the top. The *Maestà* had been removed from the Duomo by 1505, and its two faces were sawn apart in 1771. The small panel shown here, which originally formed part of the back predella, was probably one of the last elements of the altarpiece to be executed. It has long been separated from the main body of the front and the back, which remains in Siena (in the Museo dell'Opera del Duomo) to this day. For all its attention to detail, therefore, it was always intended to be a minor part of a far larger whole.

The panel shows the rarely-represented scene of Christ sitting barefoot at Jacob's Well outside the city of Sychar, as recounted in the fourth chapter of the Gospel according to Saint John. Christ is shown in conversation with the Woman of Samaria who carries a water bucket in her left hand and balances an earthenware jug on her head. He is probably to be thought of as uttering the famous words: 'Whosoever drinketh of this water shall thirst again: But whosoever drinketh of the water that I shall give him shall never thirst.' On the right are the disciples emerging from the city to which they had gone in search of food; they are carrying bread rolls in their cloaks. The style of the panel, and especially its glowing colours, still depend upon Byzantine precedents, but the expressive quality of the faces and the comparative sophistication of the perspective, both in the cityscape and in the remarkable octagonal well, are entirely Duccio's.

ALBRECHT DÜRER

19. CHRIST AMONG THE DOCTORS

Born 1471 in Nuremberg
Died 1528 in Nuremberg

Poplar panel, 67.5×80 cm
At the lower left, on the paper that emerges from the book is marked the date '1506', with the monogram, 'AD', and the words 'opus quinque dierum' (the work of five days)
Acquired in 1935

This panel, which is signed with Dürer's famous 'AD' monogram and dated '1506', bears a further and much more unusual inscription. The artist boasts that it is 'opus quinque dierum'—'the work of five days'.

We know that Dürer made his second journey to Italy in 1506, staying for much of the time in Venice, where he executed his masterly, but now much damaged, altarpiece, the *Feast of the Rose Garlands* (Narodnygalerie, Prague). Until recently it was assumed that this picture was painted in Venice too, but a drawn copy of it suggests that the inscription on the scrap of paper protruding from the foremost doctor's book originally included the word 'Romae'. If so, it must have been painted towards the end of the year, because a letter written by Dürer to his Nuremberg friend Willibald Pirckheimer on 13 October finds him still in Venice, and indeed various factors confirm the continuing influence of that city. The dramatic half-length treatment of this particular subject against a dark background was not unknown in Northern Italy at this date. The ultimate source for the invention would appear to have been Leonardo da Vinci, and related treatments by his Milanese follower, Bernardino Luini, and the Venetian Cima da Conegliano are known. Even the choice of a poplar panel is significant; poplar was commonly used as a support for paintings in Italy, but not north of the Alps.

However, for all its dependence on Italian models, Dürer's picture is almost defiantly his own work, and must have seemed resolutely un-Italian to a contemporary audience. Although the more subdued lighting of the figures behind Christ is meant to suggest depth, and space is counterfeited by changes of scale, little attempt is made to organise the grotesque heads of the aged Doctors around Jesus into a coherent whole. Rather, each works as an individual, and there is a considerable range of expression, from the near-caricature of the warty profile head with its horrible gap-toothed grin to the far more noble incomprehension of the older sages in the foreground. No less remarkable is the bearded figure in the top right corner, which is a sort of homage to Giovanni Bellini, whom Dürer described in a letter of this very year as 'very old and still the best in painting'. The heart of the picture, however, is the conflict between Christ's youthful hands enumerating the points of his argument, and the gnarled old hands of his most sinister opponent who is certainly not yet 'astonished at his understanding and answers'. Christ himself has a cruciform halo, but is otherwise notable for His lack of idealisation, especially by comparison with Italian examples; he also departs from convention by not engaging our gaze. Dürer's virtuosity may have allowed him to complete the panel in five days, but he prepared himself well beforehand, as an exquisitely detailed drawing of hands for the work (Germanisches Nationalmuseum, Nuremberg) testifies.

Born 1599 in Antwerp
Died 1641 in London

Canvas, 117 × 101 cm
Acquired before 1930

According to the engraving made of this portrait by Adrien Lommelin in 1654, it was executed in 1631, the year before Van Dyck paid his second visit to London, and then settled there. The sitter is Jacques Le Roy, a prominent figure in the Spanish Netherlands, who held numerous important offices, the most prestigious of them being his presidency of the 'Chambres des Comptes du Brabant', to which he was appointed in 1633. The year before this portrait was painted he became the Lord of Herbaix with the title of 'Seigneur'. Van Dyck also painted portraits of the sitter's natural son Philippe Le Roy in 1630, and in the following year of the latter's bride, Marie de Roet. This magnificent pair of full-length likenesses of the young couple are now to be counted among the greatest masterpieces of the Wallace Collection in London. While it is possible that this splendid half-length was also commissioned by Philippe, it is at least as likely that the sitter had it painted for himself.

In this work, Van Dyck manages to combine the best qualities of both his native school, which he had learnt as a pupil of Rubens, and of the Italian masters whose works he had admired during his years in Italy. Jacques Le Roy in shown seated three-quarter length in a substantial chair whose red back almost blends into the similar colour of the opulent curtain. A clear pentimento behind his left shoulder indicates a change of mind: originally, the chair would have been parallel to the picture plane. He is wearing a plain black gown luxuriously edged with brown fur, from which his sleeves protrude. His relaxed pose gives his hands and his white cuffs an unforced prominence. His right hand hangs langorously free, while in his left he holds a folded sheet of paper, presumably a letter. Above the carefully-observed detail of his wide ruff, which serves as a frame, is his fine head. The sitter is shown full face, but does not confront our gaze, looking instead almost abstractedly to one side. The flesh is painted with considerable realism, and its texture contrasts effectively with the softness of his greying hair and beard on the one hand, and the unyielding quality of the ruff on the other. Van Dyck's reputation as a flatterer is certainly not completely unjustified, and although in a case like this we have no other means of knowing what the sitter looked like, we may be inclined to wonder whether the artist did not somewhat improve on nature. No doubt Jacques Le Roy was delighted, and it is hard to believe his gain has not been ours as well.

Born 1563 in Pisa
Died 1639 in London

Canvas, 120 × 168.5 cm
Acquired in 1977

By 1621, Orazio Gentileschi was one of the foremost painters in Rome. In February of that year, with the election of Alessandro Ludovisi as Pope Gregory XV, there can have seemed no reason to doubt that artists from his native Bologna would receive papal preferment. Later in the same year Giovan Antonio Sauli, an aristocratic patron, invited Orazio Gentileschi to leave Rome and come and work in his home town of Genoa. Under the circumstances, it must have been an offer Orazio found it impossible to refuse.

This canvas is one of a number painted for Sauli, and is also the first and smallest of an impressive sequence of variations on the theme of Lot and his daughters. From the time of Altdorfer (cat. 1) and Cranach (cat. 14) onwards, Lot's daughters' incestuous seduction of their father in order to perpetuate the human race had been a favourite pretext for an erotic picture, but Gentileschi treated it with a rare—if for him characteristic—modesty. For although his art was profoundly influenced by that of Caravaggio (cat. 10) he was never attracted by his violence, nor by the ribaldry of his northern followers. There are three closely similar versions of this design (the others are in the Gemäldegalerie, Berlin-Dahlem and the National Gallery of Canada, Ottawa), and it is only in a later treatment in the Museo de Bellas Artes, Bilbao, that one of the daughters is actually depicted beginning to undress. Here, instead, the figures are shown at the mouth of the cave in Zoar, where we are told they dwelt, and what is evidently meant to be the elder daughter is shown pointing into the distance, where Sodom and Gomorrah are to be imagined in flames. Lot himself is already asleep, presumably in accordance with the passage in the Book of Genesis where it is stated that 'he (Lot) perceived not when she (his daughter) lay down, nor when she arose', a verse most artists were only too happy to ignore. Only the younger sister's bare shoulders and legs hint at what is to come, just as the discarded wine-bottle and bowl allude to what has just taken place. The contrast between the urgency of the girl's expression and movement and Lot's abandonment to sleep is brilliantly managed, while the bold, simple areas of plain but bright colour against the neutral backdrop of rocks focus our attention on the deliberately intricate and rather self-conscious grouping of the three actors in the drama.

FRANCISCO JOSÉ DE GOYA Y LUCIENTES

22. ASENSIO JULIÁ

Born 1746 at Fuendetodos,
near Saragossa
Died 1828 in Bordeaux

Canvas, 54.5 × 41 cm
At the lower left the inscription: 'Goya a su Amigo Asensi'
Acquired in 1971

Goya inscribed this intimate little portrait 'Goya a su Amigo Asensi', and there appears to be no serious reason to doubt that it represents his personal friend and only real pupil, Asensio Juliá. Juliá, who was born in 1767 and died in 1830, came from Valencia, and was nicknamed 'El Pescadoret' (the little fisherman) after his father's profession. Not a great deal is known about his independent career as a painter; broadly speaking he was a follower of Goya who painted and engraved copies of his works. He also collaborated with the master on the decoration of the cupola of the Franciscan church of San Antonio de la Florida, then on the outskirts of Madrid, which was to prove Goya's last great achievement in fresco. Goya is known to have started work on the dome on 1 August 1798, and completed it by the end of October or the beginning of November of the same year.

It has been suggested that for this portrait he chose to show Juliá standing at the foot of the scaffolding, and the idea seems a plausible one. Certainly the man represented here is a painter, as the mixing-bowl with its accent of red colour and the brushes apparently casually discarded at his feet indicate, and his appearance does not conflict with Asensio Juliá's known age at the time. The full-length image does not strive to achieve the penetrating and almost painful intensity of many of Goya's close-up portraits, and instead prefers to place the figure against an unevenly lit backdrop of considerable complexity. Juliá is casually attired in a sort of painter's robe, whose rich chocolate colour and bright blue edging stand out against the more muted tones beyond. From beneath the robe there peep out touches of white at the neck and at the ankles just above his stylish black shoes with bows. He avoids our gaze and instead looks sharply sideways, as if his attention has all of a sudden been distracted. Goya was to paint one further likeness of Asensio Juliá (Sterling and Francine Clark Institute, Williamstown, Massachussetts) which is signed and dated 1814. The sitter is considerably older than here, but both pictures would appear to represent the same individual.

FRANCISCO JOSÉ DE GOYA Y LUCIENTES

23. EL TÍO PAQUETE

Born 1746 in Fuendetodos,
near Saragossa
Died 1828 in Bordeaux

Canvas, 39 × 31 cm
Acquired in 1935

On 27 February 1819, Goya acquired a small country house, or 'quinta', on the outskirts of Madrid, which became known as 'La Quinta del Sordo' (The house of the Deaf Man), on account of the artist's deafness. He gave the house to his grandson Mariano, his son Francisco Javier's son, on 17 September 1823. In the intervening years he had executed a remarkable series of mural decorations in oil on the plaster of the walls of two rooms, one on the ground and the other on the first floor of the house. These powerfully haunting pictures, which were detached from the walls, transferred to canvas and in 1881 donated to the Prado, are among Goya's most astonishing achievements. They have come to be known as the 'Black Paintings', partly because of their sombre overall tonalities, but also because of the bleakness, cruelty and mystery of their subject-matter. It is to their sinister world that the leering, grimacing *Tío Paquete* belongs, probably executed in the same years, 1820-1823.

The back of the original canvas, which was relined in the last century, bore the inscription 'El célebre ciego fijo', and it has consequently been possible to identify the famous blind man as 'Old' (literally 'Uncle') Paquete. He was a blind beggar who sat on the steps of the Church of San Felipe el Real in Madrid; his celebrity derived from his singing and guitar playing. His appeal was such that he was popular as an entertainer in the most fashionable circles of the capital and was frequently invited to perform in the houses of the rich. His grinning, gap-toothed face lurches out at us, and almost seems to be shaking with laughter. His sightless eyes and the shapeless lump of his nose only serve to accentuate the grotesqueness of his appearance. Yet this is no caricature. For all the pitiless accuracy of its observation, this portait is full of humanity. As with Velazquez's representations of dwarves, with which it has so justly been compared, this image confers a sense of dignity on an individual most of Goya's contemporaries would have shied away from. The colour-range is simple, the flesh tones being framed by the intense black of the costume and the background, and by the bright grey of collar and hair, but the paint is applied with extraordinary passion in thick layers of impasto. It is hard not to believe that, in this almost frightening portrait, Goya was responding to a plight he knew only too well, that of the helpless old outcast who nevertheless does not give up.

EL GRECO
(Domenikos Theotokopoulos)

24. THE ANNUNCIATION

Born 1541 in Candia, Crete
Died 1614 in Toledo

Canvas, 117 × 98 cm
Acquired in 1975

Domenikos Theotokopoulos, known as 'El Greco' after his country of origin, is recorded as being in Venice in 1568 and is likely to have spent almost a decade in Italy, before departing for Spain. The style that he evolved in Italy managed to combine the influences of the great Venetian masters, Titian, Tintoretto and Veronese, with the icon-painting tradition of his native Crete. In this canvas, the Virgin is seated uneasily to the left of the composition and has been interrupted in her reading of a large book, which rests on a plain wooden lectern. She wears a rich blue robe with a yellowish-green lining. Behind her is a rose-red curtain that flutters in the breeze and is consumed by the cloudy radiance beyond it. The Virgin is both surprised and concerned, in accordance with the account in Chapter I of Saint Luke's Gospel, verses 28 and 29: 'And the angel came in unto her, and said, Hail, thou that art highly favoured, the Lord is with thee: blessed art thou among women. And when she saw, she was troubled at his saying, and cast in her mind what manner of salutation this should be.' Above her, three diminutive winged cherubs hover and rest on the clouds, while through a break in them the Dove of the Holy Spirit flies towards her. Over to the right the Archangel Gabriel delivers his greeting, gesturing with his right hand and holding a tall sceptre crowned with jewels in his left. The purity of his face seen in profile is other-wordly, and contrasts admirably with the all too human complexity of the Virgin's twisting attitude. He is clad in a splendidly vibrant yellow which picks up the celestial radiance, just as the pink of his sash echoes the colour of the curtain. The exterior setting, with an elegantly tiled floor leading to a low balustrade, is typical of Venetian paintings of the Annunciation, which also tend to emphasise the dramatic possibilities of the subject. It would be wrong, however, to look for a specific source. The Annunciation is habitually shown in art with the Angel on the left and the Virgin on the right, but there are exceptions, and in all El Greco's early representations of the theme the action moves from right to left. Two earlier versions (Museo del Prado, Madrid, and Julio Muñoz Collection, Barcelona) are closely related to each other, the first being a preparatory sketch for the second, and have much in common with this picture. All three versions, and particularly the pose of the Virgin in that of the Thyssen-Bornemisza Collection, would seem to relate to a triptych in the Galleria Estense in Modena. The attribution of this latter work is controversial, but if, as seems possible, it is by El Greco, it must precede the Thyssen-Bornemisza canvas, and represent some sort of a starting-point for all the other versions.

EL GRECO
(Domenikos Theotokopoulos)

25. THE ANNUNCIATION

Born 1541 in Candia, Crete
Died 1614 in Toledo

Canvas, 114 × 67 cm
The embroidered ribbon of the basket bears the inscription in Greek letters,
'O Kheretismos' (The Annunciation)
Acquired in 1954

In December 1596 El Greco received the commission for the high altarpiece of the Colegio de Doña María de Aragón in Madrid, so called after the lady who founded it. He was to be responsible both for the elaborate architectural frame with sculptural decoration and for the painting of the ensemble, and was expected to complete it by Easter 1599; in the event the Augustinians had to wait until the following year for it to be finished. Long since dismembered, originally it was possibly a triptych, with the *Annunciation* (now in the Museo Balaguer at Villanueva y Geltrú) in the centre in honour of the church's dedication to Nuestra Señora de la Encarnación, probably with the *Adoration of the Shepherds* (now in the Bucharest Museum) on the left and the *Baptism of Christ* (now in the Prado, Madrid) on the right.

This *Annunciation* is a very finished study for the central composition, almost identical to the final version, but smaller in scale and painted on canvas. It is a remarkably fine example of El Greco's mature style as it evolved in Spain, with its luminous blocks of pure colour and extraordinarily elongated forms, in the past often supposed to be the product of the artist's astigmatism, but now much more convincingly associated with his reading of the ancient philosopher Pseudo-Dionysius the Areopagite. This philosopher claimed to be the Dionysius who was converted to Christianity after hearing Saint Paul preach on the Areopagus at Athens, and his treatises were generally regarded in the sixteenth century as second only to the New Testament. He conceived the illumination of the soul in terms of light metaphysics. Initially, radiant light emanates from God and is imported to angels, who transmit it to man whose soul is thus spiritually illuminated. This celestial process he likened to a flame. At the foot of the composition, in addition to the conventional work-basket, which alludes to the Virgin's role as a ward of the Temple, for which she made a new veil, is another Marian attribute, the burning bush. It refers back to God speaking to Moses out of the burning bush. This is a peculiarly appropriate symbol for El Greco to have chosen: the bush which burned but, miraculously, was not consumed by the flames, is here a symbol of the Virgin who conceived by the Holy Spirit but was not consumed by the flames of concupiscence. A ribbon below it bears an inscription in Greek letters reading 'O Kheretismos', that is 'The Annunciation'. This area is comparatively naturalistically rendered, as if in order to ease the transition between the real world and that inhabited by heavenly beings. Here the Virgin is already lifted on to a higher spiritual plane than any ordinary mortal, and converses serenely with the hesitant emerald-clad Archangel Gabriel. Above and between them the Dove of the Holy Spirit cleaves a radiant path through the solid-seeming, cherub-filled clouds, while in the highest heaven a concert of angels sing praises, to the accompaniment of a veritable small orchestra of instruments: recorder, clavichord, mandolin, harp, and viola da gamba.

Born between 1580 and 1585
in Antwerp
Died 1666 in Haarlem

Canvas, 83.5 × 67.5 cm
Acquired before 1930

A number of paintings of fishermen, boys and girls, by no means all of them definitely by the artist, have been associated with the name of Frans Hals, and generally dated around 1630. Of these, by far the closest to the *Fisherman Playing the Violin* is the *Laughing Fisherboy* in the Collection of the Prince zu Bentheim und Steinfurt at Burgsteinfurt in Westphalia. Both share the same liveliness of expression, have equally unruly blue bonnets on their heads of a kind commonly worn by fisherfolk, and are shown against comparable landscape backgrounds. This type of setting is highly unusual in Hals's single portraits, and some critics have even gone so far as to argue that the landscape was painted by another hand, the artist in question being supposed to be Pieter Molyn. One objection to this view, albeit not an insuperable one, is the fact that the landscape was not added after the completion of the figure, which visibly overlaps it at various points. Even more tellingly, perhaps, the rather schematic and summary character of the beach scene does not suggest that it is the work of a landscape specialist, and indeed it appears to be all of a piece with the rest of the canvas. The tower that rises above the dunes looks like an actual landmark, and it has been proposed that it represents the beacon near Zandvoort, a village on the coast about five miles away from Haarlem. It has also been argued that the fiddler is a self-portrait, but it does not resemble any known likeness of the artist. The idea probably arose for the simple reason that the violinist is left-handed and was therefore assumed to have been derived from a mirror-image. But a left-handed peasant fiddler might have had added charm for Hals, and in any event the sitter fails to look out at us directly, as we would expect in a self-portrait, and instead gazes away to one side and almost seems to move to the sound of his own music-making. His face is delightfully full of joie-de-vivre and good humour, and although he plainly comes from a very different walk of life from *The Laughing Cavalier*, Hals's masterpiece in the Wallace Collection, London, he is no less animated or amused. The handling of the oil paint is characteristically free, not only in obvious areas of bravura such as the hat, but also in the bold strokes of the brush that conjure the violin, and even the hands, into life. Two other versions of the composition are known, neither of which is autograph.

HANS HOLBEIN THE YOUNGER

27. KING HENRY VIII

Born c. 1497 in Augsburg
Died 1543 in London

Oak panel, 28 × 20 cm
Acquired in 1934

It is no exaggeration to say that the history of English painting in the sixteenth and seventeenth centuries is saved from ignominy by a succession of artists from abroad. And although the great Rubens (cat. 39) did come and paint for King Charles I, it is Holbein and Van Dyck (cat. 20) who left the greatest mark, not only upon our native art, but also on our sense of our own history. It is impossible to think of Henry VIII, his wives and his court without summoning up images of paintings and drawings by Holbein, just as Charles I and Henrietta Maria are indissolubly linked in our imaginations with Van Dyck. In both cases it requires a great effort of will to go beyond the mythology and seek out the reality. There is an unexpected difference between Holbein and Van Dyck in this connection, however; whereas countless representations of Charles I and Henrietta Maria from the latter's brush have come down to us, this oak panel is the only universally accepted autograph likeness of Henry VIII painted by Holbein to survive, and was probably executed not long after the beheading of Anne Boleyn on 19 May 1536. Holbein painted a portrait of Jane Seymour around this time, which is now in the Kunsthistorisches Museum, Vienna, but the two cannot have been designed as a pair, on account of the difference in scale between them.

Holbein first came to England in 1526, but did not settle definitively in London until 1532. By 1536 he had become Henry's official court painter. In this panel he portrays the King on a small scale, with a delicacy of touch and an attention to detail that are worthy of a miniaturist and remind us that Holbein did indeed practice that art. But the consequent effect is of grandeur and monumentality: the King seems about to erupt and burst free of the confines of the picture-space. There is barely a sliver of blue background above his head, his broad shoulders are not contained by the sides of the picture and his heavily be-ringed hands are only partially visible at its bottom limit. Nevertheless, for all the majesty and splendour of the costume, which is covered with fur, rubies, silver and gold, it is the head which commands our attention. Henry looks out directly and piercingly at us with small cold eyes lost in a sea of face. He is not shown completely frontally, and the turn of his head only serves to accentuate its awesome bulk. It is not a flattering likeness, but it was evidently one that pleased the King, for it was repeated in the cartoon (a fragment of which is preserved in the National Portrait Gallery in London) for the now destroyed Whitehall Palace mural .

PIETER DE HOOCH

28. THE COUNCIL CHAMBER OF THE AMSTERDAM TOWN HALL

Born 1629 in Rotterdam
Died after 1684 in Amsterdam

Canvas, 112.5 × 99 cm
Signed at the lower left: 'P.D. Hooch'
Acquired in 1960

Pieter de Hooch is best known for his sensitive handling of the theme of the Dutch interior, as it had been perfected by Vermeer, who, like him, lived and worked in Delft. After 1660, however, de Hooch moved to Amsterdam, where he executed the present canvas, probably around the middle of the decade. In marked contrast to the artist's staple diet of quiet representations of private households or small courtyards, this picture is one of a number which show various parts of the Town Hall in Amsterdam, now the Royal Palace. It is exceptional for its grandeur of scale, with the result that the figures are positively dwarfed by the expansiveness of the space which they inhabit. The room in which the scene is set is the Council Chamber, and de Hooch has included various details that are still readily identifiable. The most prominent of these is the large painting over the fireplace, which represents the suitably republican subject of the *Roman Consul Caius Fabricius Lucullus at the Camp of Pyrrhus*. According to the account of the ancient writer Valerius Maximus, Fabricius was both bribed and threatened by the King of Epirus, but remained a model of integrity and *continentia* throughout. The picture in question was painted by Rembrandt's pupil, Ferdinand Bol, in 1656, and below it there were inscribed appropriate verses by Holland's greatest poet, Joost van den Vondel, which are just legible in the present canvas. The burgomasters sat at the table in front of the fire which is partially visible. Light comes into the room from the right, and the shutters which covered only the lower part of the windows are opened inwards. It is not clear what the various people in the picture are doing, and they may simply be visitors, especially since one of them, a man in a tall black hat, seems to be pointing something out to his nervous-looking female companion. Furthermore, the most prominent of them, the man with sword and stick in the foreground, appears to be looking up intently at the picture that faced the Bol, Govaert Flinck's equally republican *Marcus Curtius Dentatus Refusing the Gifts of the Samnites*. In any event there can be no doubt that de Hooch took exceptional care over the placement of these figures, and even bothered to move the dog nearer to the centre of the composition. With time and the thinning of the oil pigment, the original location of the dog which he painted out has become apparent, so that it is visible as a ghostly presence. The recession into the light-filled room beyond is effortlessly managed, and even the artist's signature on one of the floor-tiles in the bottom left-hand corner is rendered in perspective. Despite the designation of many of Pieter de Hooch's works as 'slices of life', the overall effect of this work is considerably more ambitious, and the theatrical swags of the large orange curtain in the foreground have little to do with humdrum reality.

First recorded 1496 in Simancas
Died 1519 in Palencia, Castile

Oak panel, 31.5 × 22 cm
Acquired before 1930

The history of this panel is intimately connected with that of a pair of portraits in the Kunsthistorisches Museum in Vienna. It has been convincingly argued that those in the Vienna portraits represent Philip the Fair and his wife Joanna the Mad, one of the four daughters of Queen Isabella of Castile, who married in 1496. The style of these works suggests that they are either originals, or copies of lost originals, by Juan de Flandes, who was at work in Spain from 1496, and was made Isabella's court painter in 1498. The Thyssen-Bornemisza portrait is clearly related in style to the Vienna couple, and furthermore the female sitter looks remarkably similar. It has been proposed therefore that this is an earlier representation of Joanna the Mad, but it seems more likely that it depicts one of her two younger sisters, Maria or Catherine. It is always hazardous to attempt to guess the age of people in portraits, but it is worth pointing out that Catherine, known to English history as Catherine of Aragon, was born three years after Maria in 1485. She would consequently have been about ten at the time of her sister's marriage, an acceptable age for the girl in the portrait, and indeed only fifteen at the time of her own marriage to Arthur, the Prince of Wales and Henry VIII's brother, in 1501.

Juan de Flandes, an artist unreservedly admired by no less a figure than Dürer (cat. 19), reveals both his Northern background and his mastery in this memorable likeness. He shows the young princess simply but elegantly dressed in white with black and gold edging against a sea-green background on to which deep shadows are cast. Her plain, oval face is turned slightly to one side and lit from the right. She toys with a rosebud in her right hand, of which only a couple of fingers are visible, and looks away wistfully to one side. Every detail of costume and surface is unerringly observed, but the overall effect is of tenderness and sympathy rather than pedantry. If this is a likeness of Catherine, then it is hard to resist thinking ahead to all the tragedies that lay in store for her.

30. STILL LIFE WITH CHINESE PORCELAIN BOWL AND EWER

Born 1619 in Rotterdam
Died 1693 in Amsterdam

Canvas, 109 × 81.5 cm
Acquired in 1981

Although it is neither signed nor dated, this is one of the most lavish still lifes of Kalf's maturity, executed some years after he settled in Amsterdam in 1653. It is of a type that the Dutch call 'Pronkstilleven', which literally translated means 'show still life'. In one sense it conforms to the type that Kalf made peculiarly his own in its combination of rich Turkey carpets spread carelessly over tables, and topped by Chinese porcelain and fruit, invariably including a peeled lemon with its sinuous tail of rind. In another sense, however, it is unique. Like many of his fellow artists, Kalf was a dealer in works of art as well as a painter and it is generally—and no doubt correctly—assumed that the various objects that recur in picture after picture were part of his stock. By contrast, the Chinese porcelain bowl and ewer which figure so prominently in this canvas are never repeated. Even in Kalf's time they would have been already regarded as exceptionally rare collectors' pieces, and they have subsequently attracted the attention of scholars of ceramics. Both can be dated to the second half of the sixteenth century and have been adorned with European mounts. The ewer is very like one that belonged to Shah Abbas the Great in Ardebil, and is now in Tehran, while the bowl is virtually identical to one now in the Metropolitan Museum of Art, New York. Like the one in Kalf's picture, it too has mounts that suggest Elizabethan England, and it has been argued that both bowls must originally have belonged to the Burghley House Collection. How Kalf came across these treasures remains a mystery. Beyond the two Chinese porcelain pieces is a splendid Nautilus cup surmounted by a figure of Neptune with his trident, and further back still are two goblets of wine. A pocket-watch is also prominent on the table. However, any hint of 'Vanitas' in the picture is more than compensated for by the general sense of opulence. Kalf's technique is almost worthy of Vermeer in its attention to detail and its awareness of the broader effect, as bright areas of colour and light emerge from a warm surrounding darkness.

Born 1494 in Leiden

Died 1533 in Leiden

Oak panel, 29.8 × 39.5 cm

Acquired in 1971

In the early sixteenth century the vast majority of paintings, and even of drawings and prints, fell into three broad categories, namely religious works, historical and mythological subjects, and portraits. This small panel, which appears to represent a simple game of cards, satisfies none of these classifications, and that is doubtless the reason why some scholars have felt the need to confer a deeper meaning upon it.

One line of argument starts from the presumption that the three gamblers are prominent figures from contemporary history. The man on the left, according to this interpretation, is Charles V of Spain, the man opposite him is Cardinal Wolsey, and the woman is Margaret of Austria, the Regent of the Netherlands (the letters 'FM' on the trimming to the bodice of her dress are deemed to stand for 'Filia Maximiliani'). The game of cards consequently becomes a covert means of illustrating a political allegory, and even the fleurs-de-lis on the table, which symbolise France, are not without significance. Yet it is hard to believe that this modest little picture was intended to enshrine such complexities. Apart from anything else, card players and chess players were favourite subjects of Lucas's (a characteristic example is in the collection of the Earl of Pembroke at Wilton House), but none of the others gives the slightest indication of having been devised as a topical *roman-à-clef*.

A more plausible if less ingenious explanation would see the game of cards as a way of expressing the amorous rivalry of the two men for the favours of the young woman who sits between them. She has just played a knave of spades, and seems to encourage the young man to play his king and win the trick against his older rival's eight.

Above all, however, what impresses is the work's genuine novelty as a very early, and understandably not entirely confident depiction of a scene from everyday life. Against a background of trees and cloudless blue sky, the three figures are comfortably placed round a table that tilts rather precariously towards us. They are all fashionably as well as colourfully dressed, with reds, oranges and greens predominating, and seem totally absorbed in their play. Already the sense of mild intrusion we feel when looking at the best genre paintings begins to play a part in the picture's appeal. An early copy of the composition was formerly in the collection of the late A.F. Philips at Eindhoven in Holland.

MASTER OF FLEMALLE
(Robert Campin)
(attributed to)

32. PORTRAIT OF A MAN

Born c. 1380 in Tournai
Died 1444 in Tournai

Oak panel, 35 × 24 cm including frame
Acquired in 1960

The sitter has been identified as Robert de Masmines on the basis of the supposed resemblance between this portrait and one in a later compilation of portrait drawings called the *Recueil d'Arras*. A fair amount is known about Robert: he was in the service of the Dukes of Burgundy, John the Fearless and Philip the Good, became a Knight of the Golden Fleece in 1430 and died later that year at the Siege of Bouvignes. Unfortunately, the resemblance between the two likenesses is tenuous in the extreme.

The style of the work certainly suggests that of the Master of Flémalle, now generally identified as Robert Campin, who is documented as the teacher of both Rogier van der Weyden (cat. 53) and Jacques Daret (cat. 16). There is another, virtually identical portrait in the Gemäldegalerie, Berlin-Dahlem. It is not at all easy to distinguish between the two in terms of quality, and it may well be that both the Berlin and Thyssen-Bornemisza portraits are very early copies of a now lost original. It is undeniably the case that the pair of portraits of a man and a woman in the National Gallery, London, universally accepted as the work of the Master of Flémalle, reveal greater technical finesse and a more sophisticated understanding of the ways in which character may be conveyed through facial expression. On the other hand, the meticulous attention to surface detail in such particulars as the fur-trimmed clothing, the hair, stubble, and even the wrinkles, as well as the way the bulky head of the sitter almost fills the picture-space, all suggest the world of the Master of Flémalle. It is a notable feature of this portrait that it is still in its original wooden frame, which is painted to simulate porphyry, and is continuous with the picture surface.

33. POSTHUMOUS PORTRAIT OF WENCESLAS OF LUXEMBOURG, DUKE OF BRABANT

Probably active c. 1405 to c. 1415

Oak (?) panel transferred to cradled masonite panel, 34.4 × 25.4 cm
Acquired in 1956

The back of the panel on which this profile portrait was painted originally bore the inscription 'Wenchcaius dux Brabanciae in antiquitate 34rum annorum', which allows us to identify the sitter. Wenceslas was born in Prague in 1337. Through the preferment of his elder brother, the Emperor Charles IV, and his marriage to Joanna, the daughter of the Duke of Brabant, he became Duke of Luxembourg in 1354 and Duke of Brabant in 1355. Ineffectual as a ruler, he is best remembered as the protector of such literary figures as Froissart and Eustache Deschamps. He died in 1383 at the age of 46.

The style of this portrait, and indeed of the costume, suggests a date of around 1405-1415, so it must be based on a lost original. Its most original feature, the upward gaze and tilt of the head, suggests that the likeness must have been derived from a donor portrait that formed part of a larger whole. That this image is not a fragment is proved by the fact that the gesso preparation of the panel is visible on all four sides if the frame is removed. It was customary in such portraits to update the costume, so no doubt the hat and fur-trimmed tunic are new; they conform to the fashions of the first years of the fifteenth century. On the other hand blue was Wenceslas's favourite colour; he was known as the 'Blue Duke'. The artist, who remains anonymous—although the name of Jean Malouel, court painter to Philip the Bold of Burgundy, has been proposed—shows great gifts in being able to animate a second-hand likeness and convince us of its truth to life. It seems reasonable to suppose that such a portrait would have been commissioned by someone with a dynastic connection with Wenceslas, and an obvious candidate is Philip's son, Anthony of Burgundy, who was Wenceslas's successor and commissioned the construction of his tomb. In support of this hypothesis, it is worth pointing out that what would appear to be this portrait was part of the collection of Margaret of Austria, daughter of Mary of Burgundy and granddaughter of Charles the Bold, in the early part of the sixteenth century.

WESTPHALIAN MASTER

34a. THE VIRGIN OF THE HORTUS CONCLUSUS AND CHRIST ON THE CROSS
(Left-hand panel of diptych)

Active first quarter of the fifteenth century

Oak panel, 28.7 × 18.5 cm
Acquired before 1930

These two gold ground pictures, now framed as one, may originally have formed part of a larger whole. They were painted in the early years of the fifteenth century by an as yet unidentified artist from Westphalia who worked in the circle of the painter of the Frondenberg altarpiece (executed between 1410 and 1421), who was in turn inspired by Konrad von Soest. They are remarkable for their density of iconographic allusion, so that nowadays only the most initiated of spectators are able to look at them without being in need of a good deal of explanation. On the left-hand panel (cat. 34a) Mary ('Sancta Maria' as it is inscribed in Gothic script in her halo) is seated with her Son, surrounded by various symbols of her virginity, most of which are the result of interpreting passages in the Old Testament as anticipations of events in the New. The main one is the 'Hortus Conclusus' or 'Garden Inclosed', which derives from a reference to the beloved as a 'Garden Inclosed' in the Song of Solomon. Within the garden itself is another from the Song of Solomon, the 'fountain sealed', as well as the 'Rose and the Fleece of Gideon'. Up above, and represented even less realistically, are the Closed Gate of Ezekiel, the Ark of the Covenant, Aaron's Flowering Rod on the altar, and God speaking to Moses out of the heart of the Burning Bush. On the right-hand panel (cat. 34b) Christ is shown on the cross, surrounded by yet more symbolic details, many of them arranged to left and right of Him in opposed pairs. Thus, the figure of a woman carrying a banner and a chalice with a church above her head stands for 'Ecclesia', while on the other side the slumped man, wearing a blindfold and surmounted by a broken banner, up above which there is a skull through which the serpent with the apple is crawling, represents the Synagogue. Similarly, the haloed lamb with the book with the seals from the Book of Revelation refers to the new religion of Christ, while the sacrificial animal on the altar refers to the Old Dispensation. Finally, at the top are two vignettes, one of the Virgin handing the Pope a consecrated Host, the other of Eve proffering a skull to the aged Adam. As well as the foliage that grows forth from the cross, each of its four arms terminates in a hand. The one above has the key to heaven, the one on the right of Christ is raised in benediction, the one on His left holds a sword, and the one below beats death (yet another skull) with a wooden mallet. The style throughout is intimate, delicate and other-worldly to the point of naïvety, as perhaps befits the subject-matter.

WESTPHALIAN MASTER

34b. THE VIRGIN OF THE HORTUS CONCLUSUS
AND CHRIST ON THE CROSS
(Right-hand panel of diptych)

Active first quarter of the fifteenth
century

Oak panel, 28.7 × 18.5 cm
Acquired before 1930

(For catalogue note see cat. 34a)

HANS MEMLING

Born c. 1433 in Seligenstadt,
near Frankfurt-am-Main
Died 1494 in Bruges

35a. (Recto)
PORTRAIT OF A YOUNG MAN

Oak panel, 29 × 22.5 cm
Acquired in 1938

This magnificent double-sided panel almost certainly originally formed part of a triptych, or less probably, a diptych. It shows a young man kneeling in prayer, possibly before a representation of the Virgin and Child on a separate panel which is now lost, and very probably with a portrait of his wife in a third panel on the other side. This type of half-length devotional image appears to have been devised by the Netherlandish painter Rogier van der Weyden, but it was perfected by Memling, by whom many examples, almost all of them alas dismembered, are known. The donor, who is fashionably dressed in a black fur gown over an elaborate gold and white shirt, is shown in three-quarter face, and we may suspect that Memling did not find it easy to reconcile achieving a convincing likeness of the sitter with making him appear to communicate with the Virgin and Child. Similarly, it is essential that the young man's hands be included, but as a result the head is over-large for the body that supports it. The hands themselves, however, are painted with characteristic refinement, and the foreshortening of the left arm and its gilded sleeve is managed with considerable finesse. Behind the figure is an opening onto a landscape, framed by a squat porphyry column with gilded base and capital; an oriental carpet is draped over the sill. The view affords us a glimpse of the light and air of the world beyond, but in no way distracts attention from the intense, thoughtful head of the young man, framed by a splendid shock of painstakingly delineated hair.

The other side of the portrait (cat. 35b), which would have been visible when the triptych was closed, is one of the most haunting of all early Netherlandish still lifes. Given its sacred context, it is only reasonable to suppose that the three plants in the little maiolica jug, which significantly bears the 'YHS' (Jesus) monogram, are endowed with symbolic meaning. The white lilies symbolise the purity of the Virgin, the iris can refer to Mary as Queen of Heaven or—on account of its name of sword lily—as Mater Dolorosa, and the columbine ('columba' is the Latin for dove) was associated with the Holy Spirit.

Interestingly enough, an identical maiolica jug appears in a picture of the *Virgin and Child* (Gemäldegalerie, Berlin-Dahlem) which is universally agreed to be by Memling or at the very least from his workshop. It has been suggested that the sitter is Italian, on account of his physiognomy and by association with the tin-glazed jug. Neither possibility is convincing; the former is highly subjective, while the latter presumes that the piece of pottery, which in any event probably belonged to the artist, was introduced as a badge of nationality. Unfortunately for this line of argument, the jug, although Italianate in type, is more likely to have been made in the Southern Netherlands by Italian expatriates. Memling's portraits are not particularly easy to date, but it is generally thought that this is a late work, probably dating from the last decade of his life.

HANS MEMLING

35b. (Verso)
STILL LIFE: MAIOLICA VASE WITH FLOWERS

Born c. 1433 in Seligenstadt,
near Frankfurt-am-Main
Died 1494 in Bruges

Oak panel, 29 × 22.5 cm
Acquired in 1938

(For catalogue note see cat. 35a)

PALMA VECCHIO
(Jacopo Negretti)

36. A YOUNG WOMAN ('LA BELLA')

Born c. 1480 in Serina,
near Bergamo
Died 1528 in Venice

Canvas, 95 × 80 cm
Inscribed on the stone parapet: 'AM.B/ND'
Acquired in 1959

Although this representation of a beautiful young woman is by no means the only one of its kind upon which a subsequent generation has bestowed the fanciful title of *La Bella*, it is certainly more than worthy of such an accolade. In the past it was paid the further compliment of being attributed to Titian, but it is now universally accepted as the work of his contemporary Palma Vecchio.

Palma Vecchio, whose real name was Jacopo Negretti, was so called posthumously in order to differentiate him from his great-grandson Palma Giovane, who was also a painter. He was born in Bergamo, a city then under Venetian jurisdiction, but soon moved to Venice, and it was there that his style was formed. Ever since the days of Antonello da Messina (cat. 2) it had been a commonplace of Venetian portraiture to picture the sitter behind a stone parapet and against a plain, dark background (in this case enlivened by an angled pilaster). Only after the turn of the century did the parapet become stepped and the viewing-distance increase, as genuine half-lengths took the place of bust-lengths which occasionally included the hands, as here and in Titian's comparable *Portrait of a Woman* in the National Gallery, London. Nor is *La Bella* unique in having letters prominently inscribed on the parapet. We do not know what the canvas's original audience understood by these letters, but it seems only reasonable to assume that they had some significance. Indeed, many details of pictures of this type, such as the way the sitter holds her flowing tresses in her right hand, may have contained meanings now lost to us. On a simple level she is performing her toilet, as the box in her left hand makes plain, but some allusion to the vanity of worldly show may well also be implied. More generally, it seems plausible that this whole class of pictures, in which an attractive young girl confronts our gaze, were not straightforward portraits. It is likely that these 'beauties' were executed for collectors more interested in idealised images of Woman than in convincing likenesses of individual women. This is a comparatively restrained example of the genre, although much is made of the girl's bare shoulder against the white of her shift. Furthermore, the rich reds and blues of her billowing drapery, not to mention the elaborate detail of her sleeves, reveal how much expense and trouble Palma Vecchio must have lavished on the picture. It probably dates from the second or third decade of the sixteenth century, and shows the artist at the height of his considerable powers.

JAN POLACK

37. PORTRAIT OF A BENEDICTINE AS SAINT BENEDICT

Born c. 1435, probably in Cracow
Died in 1519 in Munich

Fir panel, 57.3 × 41 cm
Dated at the upper edge: '1484'
Acquired in 1934

It was by no means unusual in the Renaissance for prominent members of monastic orders to have themselves portrayed holding the attributes of their respective major saints. A case in point is Giovanni Bellini's *Portrait of a Dominican* in the National Gallery, London, which originally showed the sitter holding a letter, and was subsequently transformed to endow him with the palm, dagger and machete which identify him as Saint Peter Martyr. In the same spirit, Jan Polack here depicts his black-habited Benedictine holding an open book, presumably the Rule of Saint Benedict, and more significantly with a glass containing a serpent. This alludes to the episode, distinctly reminiscent of one from the life of Saint John the Evangelist, when an attempt was made by the monks of Vicovaro to poison Saint Benedict. The fact that the artist has taken particular care over this detail is revealed by his having originally located it further to the side and drawn it on a larger scale, as the blue underdrawing now visible through the translucent pigment of the background makes apparent. The picture is dated 1484 in Gothic script along the upper margin, and was thus executed at a time when Polack—as his name would suggest, originally from Poland—was already based in Munich. The Benedictine sitter was presumably an important member of the Order, and it has convincingly been suggested that he may be the Abbot of Weihenstephan, Christoph Schleichere, who held office from 1484 to 1492, since Jan Polack was at work on the high altarpiece of his church from 1483 to 1489. He is shown three-quarter length behind a parapet and against an unusual yellow backdrop, clearly to be understood as a wall since he casts a shadow onto it. His hands are remarkable for the extraordinary elongation of their fingers, while the expression on the Abbot's face is penetrating but also decidedly melancholy, with slightly sagging cheeks and a resolutely doleful downward turn to the lips. Jan Polack was appointed official painter to the city of Munich in 1488, four years after this likeness was painted, and although admittedly an artist of the second rank, he reveals himself here as an extremely able one.

Born 1613 in Taverna, Calabria
Died 1699 in La Valetta, Malta

Canvas, 107 × 145 cm
Acquired in 1977

Mattia Preti, who was born in the south of Italy in the remote province of Calabria, probably painted this canvas in the 1630s, not long after his arrival in Rome. It is one of a number of half-length genre scenes, invariably showing musicians, dice-players, or card-players, which have been convincingly dated to this period of the artist's career. Another characteristic example is in the Ashmolean Museum, Oxford. The obvious influence is that of Caravaggio (cat. 10), and of a work such as the recently re-discovered *Cardsharps*, now in the Kimbell Art Museum, Fort Worth. Preti was also very probably familiar with pictures of a similar type by Caravaggio's followers Valentin (cat. 50) and Manfredi, but it is also worth recalling the ultimate source for all such representations, namely the sombre half-lengths, often of musicians, from the circle of Giorgione and the young Titian.

In this particular instance the boldness of the chiaroscuro, which leaves large areas of the work in stygian gloom and bathes significant details—notably heads, hands and the woman's decolletage—in bright light, is an obvious legacy from Caravaggio, as is the romantic elaboration of the figures' costumes. On the other hand, the enigmatic treatment of the subject is arguably more in tune with Venetian precedents. The exceptionally reflective young woman with her fluttering veil may be presumed to be engaged in singing a duet with the boy on her left around whom she puts her arm. Mouth open, he is totally absorbed in making music, his eyes intently fixed on the sheet of score he holds in his right hand. He wears an armoured breastplate, which suggests he is a soldier, but the significance of this particular should not be over-emphasised, because by this date it had become a commonplace of this kind of picture. Meanwhile, and rather apart from the other two, there sits the magnificently beruffed fiddler wearing a hat which sports an exceptionally resplendent pair of ostrich plumes. He looks out directly at us, seemingly distracted from his task as accompanist, although his bow remains poised at the ready. It may be suspected that the full-blooded Caravaggism of this picture would have struck the more up-to-the-minute connoisseurs of Preti's day as distinctly old-fashioned, but fortunately it possesses a brooding and romantic intensity that saves it from the charge of provincialism. Although some doubts have in the past been raised about the autograph status of the work, there seems no reason to question it as being from Preti's hand. The execution seems all of a piece, and in any event it is hard to believe that a young artist at the outset of his career would have been able to afford the luxury of using studio assistants.

PETER PAUL RUBENS

39. PORTRAIT OF A LADY WITH A ROSARY

Born 1577 in Siegen, Westphalia
Died 1640 in Antwerp

Oak panel, 107 × 76 cm
Acquired in 1979

This panel was originally one of a pair; its pendant is now in a private collection in Switzerland, and depicts a bearded man, wearing a sword and accompanied by a dog. The sitter in each portrait is turned slightly inwards and are almost certainly a husband and his wife. The style of the portrait shown here, together with the sitter's costume, are very similar to those found in the double portrait of Rubens and his first wife, Isabella Brandt, executed in 1609 (Alte Pinakothek, Munich). It would consequently seem plausible to suggest that this portrait is close to it in date. At this period, Rubens was court painter in Antwerp to the Archduke Albert and Archduchess Isabella of Austria. In 1608 he had returned home from Italy, where he had been in the service of the Gonzaga family in Mantua. The sitter here is dressed in the height of fashion (as indeed is her husband) and although it has not proved possible to identify them, there can be no doubt that they were members of the court. She is depicted three-quarter length against an opulent backdrop of red damask, and stands upright and utterly in control of her destiny. Her hair is pulled back from her forehead, and the expression on her face is one of considerable hauteur with nevertheless just the hint of a smile. She wears an impressive ruff and an even more imposing lace headdress. The plain black of her dress provides a splendid foil for the rich silver and gold floral decoration of her bodice, from which there hangs a gold chain. In her hands she holds a rosary, which suggests devotion, in spite of the prevailing atmosphere of worldliness.

Later in his career Rubens would perhaps have made the lady look less unbending, and the paint would certainly have been more freely applied. At this stage, however, he was already without rivals among his Northern contemporaries. One has only to look at the portraits of an artist such as Frans Pourbus the Younger to see what an enormous difference there is, both in the handling of the paint and in the grasp of the sitter's personality, between the pedantry of the one and the flair of the other.

SALOMON VAN RUYSDAEL   40. RIVER LANDSCAPE WITH FISHERMEN

Born between 1600 and 1603
in Naarden
Died 1670 in Haarlem

Oak panel, 51.5 × 83.5 cm
Signed and dated on the boat: 'S.v.R. 1645'
Acquired before 1930

Salomon van Ruysdael belonged to a family of landscape painters, and whereas little is known about the work of his elder brother Isaac, it is the latter's son Jacob Ruisdael who is now the most famous of them all. Nevertheless, this exceptionally well-preserved panel leaves no doubt as to what a good artist his uncle Salomon was at his best. He started comparatively slowly, but by the 1630s he had found a style of his own, and went on from strength to strength. This picture is signed and dated 'S.v.R. 1645' on the boat in the right foreground and was executed in the following decade, at a time when river scenes of fishermen plying their trade formed an important part of his output. A closely comparable example, now in the Kunsthalle at Hamburg, dates from the same year.

The picture is composed on a gentle diagonal, in such a way that our gaze moves from left to right, from the closed prospect of trees by the riverbank to the glimpse of a town in the far distance. Over to the left are two fishermen, one busy bending down in a small boat near the water's edge, the other standing on the bank and pulling in his nets. A few scattered birds linger nearby, presumably in anticipation of the catch. In the middle distance, in the shadow of a modest group of dwellings, more figures are visible, again divided between the land and the water. Finally, in the right foreground is another rowing-boat, into which are crammed two men, a woman and a huge fish basket. Beyond them, and leading away into the distance at carefully spaced intervals, are three sailing boats full of people and the same number of rowing-boats. Similarly, the colour guides the eye from left to right, away from the shadowy browns and dark greens of the riverbank, through the lighter greens of the middle ground to the luminous horizon where water and sky almost seem to blend into one another. The mood of the scene is reinforced by the mirror-calm water. The oil paint is thinly applied in the main, with the result that in some areas the ground is visible underneath. It was not Ruysdael's practice to paint actual stretches of countryside with topographical accuracy, but rather to combine various typical features of the Dutch landscape in such a way as to create a heightened sense of reality.

PIETER JANSZ.
SAENREDAM

41. THE WEST FAÇADE OF THE CHURCH OF SAINT MARY, UTRECHT

Born 1597 in Assendelft
Died 1665 in Haarlem

Wood panel, 65 × 51 cm
Signed and dated at the top of the bell tower: 'Pieter Saenredam fecit 1662'
Acquired in 1979

The limpid perfection of this painting might tempt one to take it for granted that it is a faithful representation of what the artist saw, possibly even executed on the spot. Actually, the sequence of events was considerably more complicated than that. Saenredam lived in Haarlem, and the basis for this painting and a number of others of Utrecht was a series of drawings made on a visit to the city in 1636. The preliminary drawing for this representation of the façace of the Church of Saint Mary is signed and dated 30 August 1636 and has a further inscription to the effect that one of the two barns or sheds shown in the drawing was pulled down on 12 and 13 September of the same year. The sheet is preserved in the Gemeentearchief at Utrecht.

It was only in 1662, however, that Saenredam came to execute this panel, which is inconspicuously signed and dated on the top of the bell tower. His subject was an exceptionally grand Romanesque church, started in the late eleventh century but mostly dating from the twelfth, which was demolished in the last century. Comparison of the drawing with the painting reveals slight but not significant adjustments: both sheds have been removed, three men have been added in front of the façade, and the proportions of the central rose window are not the same. Furthermore, in the drawing the single surviving tower reaches to the top of the sheet, whereas in the panel there is breathing space for the sky above it. It is only when we look at Saenredam's drawing and painting of the adjacent square, in the Teylers Stichting in Haarlem and the Boymans-van Beuningen Museum in Rotterdam respectively, that further complications arise. They reveal notable differences, and since in them the façade has a mere walk-on part, whereas here it plays a starring role, it may be supposed that what we are confronted with here is the less accurate, more improved depiction. The façade has been considerably broadened to make it look more imposing, it is flanked by invented foliage, the gable has been made less pointed, the rose more prominent, and the arcade far more regular. The proportions of the façade have been altered, and the relation of the parts to the whole emended. However, the discrepancies may simply be explained by the fact that the artist made his drawings freehand, *in situ*, and subsequently perpetuated any inaccuracies in the paintings.

Saenredam is perhaps best known for his miraculously luminous representations of the interiors of churches in Holland, but this outstanding and monumental image demonstrates that he was no less gifted as a painter of exteriors, in which he artfully blended observation with imagination.

PIETER JANSZ.
SAENREDAM

CARLO SARACENI

42. MARS AND VENUS

Born 1579 in Venice
Died 1620 in Venice

Copper, 39.8 × 54.3 cm
Acquired in 1982

In the writings of the ancient Greek author, Lucian, there is a description of an imaginary painting (the technical term for this literary device is *ekphrasis*) of the wedding of Alexander the Great and Roxane. One of the details Lucian records is that little cupids were shown playing with and dressing up in the male protagonist's armour, presumably to symbolise the triumph of love over war. In the Renaissance Lucian's *ekphrases* were understandably popular in cultivated artistic circles, because they were regarded as providing at least some information about the subject-matter and even the appearance of an irretrievably lost classical heritage. As a consequence, the subject of the Wedding of Alexander and Roxane was adopted by such artists as Raphael and Sodoma, while others translated the playful putti to their representations of the loves of Mars and Venus.

This beautifully preserved and exquisite little work, which is painted on copper, is a late example of the genre dating from the second decade of the seventeenth century. Not only does it attempt to bring Lucian's imaginary picture to life, but it also manages to combine erudite subject-matter with a wittily erotic treatment of the theme. There are two earlier paintings of Mars and Venus by Saraceni, a Venetian who came to Rome and fell under the very different influences of Elsheimer and Caravaggio (cat. 10), but this is by far the most polished of the three. To the left of the composition is a faultlessly exact perspective of an arcade, rather in the manner of certain northern painters, which leads to Vulcan's forge, a discreet reminder that the couple in the foreground are adulterers, and will eventually be caught and then exposed to the ridicule of the other gods by Venus's jealous husband. This element of tension is captured in the urgency of the statues in the niches and even in the faces on the bed-hanging, but the lovers seem oblivious to any distraction. Their clothes have been carelessly discarded about the room, and now they embrace on a spectacularly comfortable-looking bed. The whiteness of Venus's flesh is contrasted with her own flushed face and with Mars's swarthiness, especially where her right leg is swung over his left in an attitude that is both intimate and concealing. Four wingless putti amuse themselves in various ways amidst the elegant decor, while over to the left Cupid himself admires his own reflection in Mars's shield, and is shown peeing onto the god of war's helmet. Improbably enough, at least to our eyes, this final detail alluded to good fortune and fecundity, and was on occasionally included in marriage pictures.

Born 1495 in Schoorl
Died 1562 in Utrecht

Oak panel, 55 × 76 cm
Acquired before 1930

Jan van Scorel led an exceptionally interesting life, mainly by virtue of being far better-travelled than any previous Dutch painter. In 1518 he started out on a remarkable journey and went first to Nuremberg, where he met the greatest Northern artist of his time, Albrecht Dürer (cat. 19). He then proceeded to Carinthia, Venice, and Jerusalem. On the way back he settled in Rome, where his fellow countryman Pope Adrian VI put him in charge of the Vatican collection of classical antiquities. Only after the Pope's death in 1523 did he finally return home, living in Utrecht and taking holy orders first as a vicar and then as a canon.

The central group of the Virgin and Child in this panel, which was subsequently extended just above the heads of the figures and at the level of the Virgin's knees, was one of his favourite inventions. He repeated it on no less than four occasions. The first of these is a now lost triptych, formerly in the Stoop Collection at Dordrecht, in which the Virgin and Child, their poses all but identical to those of the figures here, are accompanied by the sleeping Joseph. In another version of the composition they are shown against a tree, while Joseph has been relegated to the distant background. The fact that he is accompanied by the ass makes it unambiguously apparent that the *Rest on the Flight into Egypt* is being represented. That is probably also the case in the third picture, which is in the Museum in Utrecht, and only differs from the previous one in omitting the figure of Joseph with the ass. Finally, in the present picture, the action has been moved indoors, and the Virgin and Child are seen against a bright green drapery with a dull grey wall beyond, the only hint of nature coming in the form of the bunch of daffodils in the Virgin's left hand. The most significant additions by far, however, are the male and female donors, presumably husband and wife, who flank the holy pair. Artists such as Rogier van der Weyden (cat. 53) and Hans Memling (cats. 35a and 35b) had united the Virgin and Child with donors in diptychs and even triptychs, and from there it was an obvious move for a subsequent generation to include them all in the same picture. Inevitably, the three separate elements retain a good deal of autonomy, with the result that none of the participants really seems to be aware of the others. However, colour and lighting do to an extent unify them, and the observation of the impassive faces of the donors, seen in three-quarter view, is neatly contrasted with the more animated expressions of the holy personages.

SEBASTIANO DEL PIOMBO   44. FERRY CARONDOLET AND HIS SECRETARY
(Sebastiano Luciani)

Born c. 1485 in Venice
Died 1547 in Rome

Poplar panel, 112.5 × 87 cm
Inscribed beneath the pediment of the portal: 'NOSCE OPORTUNITATEM'
Acquired in 1934

Sebastiano Luciani, invariably called del Piombo because he held the honorary office of keeper of the Papal Seal from 1531 until his death, was one of the most gifted portrait painters of the Renaissance. In the past, however, his reputation suffered because his best works were frequently attributed to more famous artists. This panel is a case in point: given to Raphael little more than a hundred years after it was painted, it was not recognised as one of Sebastiano's supreme masterpieces until the nineteenth century.

It represents Ferry Carondolet, a prominent cleric who was archdeacon of Besançon Cathedral, for which he commissioned an altarpiece, in which he is likewise portrayed, from another Italian artist, Fra Bartolommeo (cat. 4). He was also procurator of Margaret of Austria, the Regent of the Netherlands, and it was in her service that he went to Rome on a diplomatic mission that lasted from June 1511 until his recall in May 1513. At some point between these dates he must have sat to Sebastiano, who had only recently arrived in Rome himself.

A number of details reveal the sitter's identity. The letter he holds in his right hand is addressed to him, the signet ring on the little finger of that hand bears his coat-of-arms, and his motto 'Know your own good fortune' is inscribed beneath the pediment of the portal behind him. He looks out of the picture as if distracted from the reply he is in the process of dictating to the hunched figure of his secretary, who looks up at him eagerly, pen poised over the paper. In the darkness of the background, at the end of a splendid marbled colonnade, a third man enters from the side, holding a note in his hand. The dramatic solution of this double portrait (in compositional terms the third figure is unimportant) was to prove remarkably influential on later artists, with the line of succession including such notables as Titian, Pier Francesco Mola, Van Dyck (cat. 20) and Reynolds. Few, however, can have approached the brilliance of the rendering of the texture of the opulent spotted fur edging of Carondolet's gown and of the weave of the Turkey carpet covering the table. The sense of pictorial structure and the imposing classical architecture bespeak Rome and the influence of his new friend Michelangelo, but the sunlit landscape and the rustic farm buildings are a reminiscence of Sebastiano's native Venice and of his mentor Giorgione.

Born c. 1468 in Milan
Died 1524 in Milan

Poplar panel, 29.5 × 26 cm
Acquired before 1930

This portrait, which was at one time attributed to Giovanni Bellini, is now generally agreed to be the work of Andrea Solario. Andrea was the brother of the sculptor Cristoforo Solario, nicknamed 'Il Gobbo' (the Hunchback), with whom he visited Venice in the 1490s. He executed his first dated work there, a *Madonna and Child with Two Saints* of 1495, now in the Brera, Milan. This painting reveals a unique combination of local Venetian influences and Lombard elements, and although their relative proportions might vary considerably, these two strands were to remain the principal aspects of Solario's style for the rest of his career. Later, Leonardo da Vinci undeniably had a profound effect on Solario's painting, but unlike so many of his Milanese contemporaries, the younger artist never allowed himself to be overwhelmed. In 1507, Solario moved to France, and it was there that many of the greatest achievements of his maturity were accomplished; he only returned home at the end of his life.

Throughout his career, Solario was a distinguished portrait painter, and this example, although small in scale, has a genuinely commanding presence. The compositional scheme is derived from that first used in Italy by Antonello da Messina (cat. 2), and subsequently adopted by all the major Venetian painters of the last quarter of the fifteenth century. The sitter is seen half-length behind a parapet, which acts as a solid foundation for the torso of the figure, and is set against a plain black background. The face is impressively modelled by the fall of light, so that the side of the nose and chin are cast into shadow. Solario's works are not easy to place in chronological order because so few of them are dated, but it seems reasonable to assume that this is a relatively early work in view of its pronounced Venetian character.

Born c. 1626 in Leiden
Died in 1679 in Leiden

Oak panel, 55.5 × 44 cm
Acquired before 1930

Jan Steen was the son of a brewer, and a brewer and tavern-owner himself. Among all the great artists of the golden age of Dutch painting he stands out for his triumphant jollity and wit. He was immensely prolific and is perhaps best known for his crowded genre scenes, although he produced many other sorts of pictures as well.

He appears as one of the characters in a number of his own pictures, but the only example of a conventional Self-Portrait is the one in the Rijksmuseum in Amsterdam. Here, more typically, he offers himself up to our scrutiny wearing somewhat archaic clothes. This sort of costume may derive from the world of the theatre, and in particular from that of the Rederijker Kamers (literally 'rhetoricians' chambers'), groups of amateur players somewhat similar to Shakespeare's mechanicals in *A Midsummer Night's Dream*. Steen portrays himself playing a lute against an extravagant diagonal swathe of green drapery, with a table by his side, on which are to be found various books and papers, and a capacious pewter tankard, all of which are painted with characteristic delicacy of touch. His expression is outstandingly good-humoured, with more than a suggestion of drunken mirth about it, his lop-sided grin, dishevelled hair, and double chin adding up to quite a picture of disarray. It may well be that he intended to present himself to us in the guise of a Jester or Fool, and his clothes might further support this interpretation, although he has also been seen as a fortunate lover. What is not in doubt is the fact that a good deal of the mockery inherent in Steen's view of the world is in this case directed at himself. Furthermore, while the fine points of the allusions may be lost on a modern public, there is no difficulty about appreciating—in both senses of the word—the broad sweep of Jan Steen's intentions.

Born 1618 in Brussels
Died 1664 in Goa

Canvas, 76.2 × 61.6 cm
Acquired in 1981

Michael Sweerts is first documented in Rome in 1646 where he was both an *Aggregato* of the Academy of Saint Luke and one of the *Virtuosi al Pantheon*. He appears at this time to have produced scenes of Roman everyday life of the kind called *Bambocciate* after their originator Pieter van Laer, who was nicknamed Bamboccio. In 1656 he is documented in Brussels, and in 1658 he moved to Amsterdam, before departing for the island of Goa in the East Indies as a lay member of a French order of missionaries. He was not to return, and died there in 1664.

Sweerts's paintings, and especially those executed after his return to the Netherlands, are characterised by an undeniable air of mystery that accords well with the fragmentary and enigmatic information we possess about his life. At times he clearly reveals the influence of Caravaggio (cat. 10), whose works he must have admired in Rome, and at others he reminds us that he is a near-contemporary of Vermeer. It is generally assumed that this picture dates from Sweerts's final years in Amsterdam, but there cannot be any certainty on this point, nor indeed concerning the subject-matter of the work. Some critics have even argued that it represents a young man, although both the turban and the billowing sleeves are more easily associated with a woman. In her elegantly foreshortened right hand she holds a small bouquet of brightly-coloured flowers which have given rise to the plausible suggestion that the figure symbolises the Sense of Smell. It has further been assumed that it must originally have belonged to a series of canvases representing the five senses. There is a picture by Sweerts, now in the Staatsgalerie at Stuttgart, that has plausibly been seen as a depiction of the Sense of Hearing, because it shows a young woman holding a sheet of music, but it cannot ever have been *en suite* with our picture for the simple reason that it is twenty centimetres smaller both in height and width. Until other pictures in the series are discovered, therefore, it remains possible that some other meaning—a Season or Flora—was intended. Fortunately there is no problem involved in admiring the simplicity and calm of the composition, the harmony of the strong plain colours, and the wistfulness of the sideways glance.

48. ESAU SELLING HIS BIRTHRIGHT

Born 1588 in Overijssel, near
Deventer, Holland
Died 1629 in Utrecht

Canvas, 110 × 140 cm
Signed in the centre of the picture, near the bottom edge: 'HTB'
Acquired in 1980

Hendrik Ter Brugghen, the most gifted as well as the most poetic representative of the Utrecht School of the followers of Caravaggio (cat. 10), painted at least two versions of this subject. They are broadly similar in their compositional arrangement and their figure types, and the main difference between them lies in the fact that the participants are seen full-length in the other—and probably marginally earlier—canvas, which is in the Bode Museum, East Berlin. The point of departure for both pictures must have been a painting like that by a member of the Bassano family, probably Francesco, now in the Musée des Beaux-Arts at Bayeux.

In this treatment of the subject, Ter Brugghen centres the action very consciously around the candle, which forms a focus for the entire composition. In the dark penumbra of the background Isaac, unaware of the treacherous drama that is unfolding, sleeps peacefully. Meanwhile, his elder son Esau, who has returned exhausted from the hunt with his catch slung over his shoulders, sells his twin brother, Jacob, his birthright in exchange for a mess of pottage. In the Book of Genesis, Jacob says, 'Esau my brother is a hairy man and I am a smooth man', but in Ter Brugghen's picture, no such distinction is made. Jacob is seated on the left and looks up intently as he proffers the dish of food, which forms part of a spare but beautifully observed still life on the table in front of him, while his brother enters hungrily from the right, closely followed by his hound. Behind them both, her haggard and toothless profile illuminated by the candle, stands their aged mother Rebecca, who loved Jacob, carrying a bowl of olives with both hands. The use of light to achieve an effect of silence and solemnity has seldom been better managed, while the bright accents of blood red, sky blue, mustard yellow, and light and dark green stand out all the more against the enveloping gloom. Although the attribution of this haunting picture to Ter Brugghen has never been doubted, it has recently been confirmed by Ivan Gaskell's discovery of the artist's habitual 'HTB' monogram on the table leg near the bottom edge of the painting towards the centre of the canvas. It and its companion must date from around 1627, just after the *Concert* of 1626 (Hermitage, Leningrad).

Born 1696 in Venice
Died 1770 in Madrid

Canvas, 48.3 × 38.2 cm
Acquired in 1975

The story of Sophonisba was first told by Livy in his account of the Punic Wars, and became an especially popular subject with artists in the seventeenth and eighteenth centuries. Sophonisba was the daughter of the Carthaginian general, Hasdrubal, whose husband sent her a cup of poison rather than deliver her into the hands of the Roman leader Scipio Africanus. In Tiepolo's picture, which is generally dated around 1755-1760, Sophonisba has already consumed the contents of the poisoned cup, which lies discarded at her side. She swoons in the arms of her two maidservants, while to one side a pageboy looks on.

Three related drawings are preserved in the Victoria and Albert Museum; these show that Tiepolo also tried the composition the other way round. There is also a larger variant of this composition in a Private Collection in Milan, but even without it there could be no doubt that this small version was a *bozzetto*, or sketch, executed with a larger end product in mind. This is not Tiepolo's last word on the subject therefore, but the freedom and fluidity of his brushstrokes in this type of picture often have the effect of making them even more appealing than his more finished works. In this sort of picture, where a scene from ancient history or mythology is treated with a definite erotic intent (Sophonisba's bare breast does not appear in Livy), Tiepolo reveals himself as a true disciple of Veronese. The costume of the figures, the rich and luminous colours, even the gleaming whiteness tinged with pink of the neo-Palladian architecture seen through the archway are all indebted to the example of Tiepolo's great Venetian predecessor. But Tiepolo is no slavish imitator, and the lightness of touch that is such an essential part of a painting like this is not found in the works of the great Renaissance masters. No less personal is the asymmetry of the composition and the affection lavished on seemingly insignificant details. The urn in the foreground, and especially the red and white flowers, are painted with as much panache as any of the heads, even that of the tragic heroine of the piece.

VALENTIN
DE BOULOGNE

50. DAVID WITH THE HEAD OF GOLIATH

Born 1591 in Coulommiers,
Seine-et-Marne
Died 1632 in Rome

Canvas, 99 × 134 cm
Acquired before 1930

Around 1600, the Italian painter Michelangelo Merisi, better known as Caravaggio (cat. 10), created a new kind of realism in art whose influence spread beyond Italy to affect the work of artists from other countries, many of whom came to Rome to learn from his example and imitate his manner. The French painter Valentin, who is called 'de Boulogne' after his home town, arrived in Rome in 1613, and became one of the most distinguished figures of this international movement. He was immediately influenced by Caravaggio, and remained so throughout a career which culminated in the painting of an altarpiece for Saint Peter's, a commission he obtained through the patronage of Cardinal Francesco Barberini.

The subject of David had already appealed to Caravaggio's bloodthirsty tastes, but he chose to depict the hero alone contemplating the enemy giant's head held aloft in his hand. By contrast, in this canvas of the mid-1620s, Valentin shows the victorious boy David half-clad in sheepskin, having come from tending his flocks and rejected the impossibly heavy armour of Saul, confronting our gaze with all the passionate but at the same time slightly theatrical intensity of youth. In his left hand he holds the elaborately turned hilt of Goliath's gigantic sword, the weapon he had used to cut off the head of the Philistine, which he now cradles in his right hand. Although Valentin has spared us the moment of actual severing—which is more than Caravaggio did when painting Judith and Holofernes—he cannot entirely resist bloodshed, for a pool is forming on the ledge and seems to be trickling towards us. The account of the story in the seventeenth chapter of the First Book of Samuel does not make it clear who the two exotically dressed attendant figures are meant to represent, unless one of them is Abner, the captain of the host of the Children of Israel. It was Abner who brought David 'before Saul with the head of the Philistine in his hand' and if that is what Valentin intends, then we the spectators are meant to be cast, highly dramatically, in the role of Saul. The lighting of the picture, with its heavy chiaroscuro used to cast a bright light onto some areas, such as the pink sleeve of the man in a feathered cap on David's right, and to plunge others into blackness, is entirely characteristic of the mature Caravaggio and his followers, as is the atmosphere of violence and of menace.

ANTOINE WATTEAU

51. LA HALTE

Born 1684 in Valenciennes
Died 1721 at Nogent-sur-Marne

Canvas, 32 × 42.5 cm
Acquired in 1975

Since its recent restoration, it has become apparent that this composition was originally oval. However, it was engraved as a rectangle by Jean Moyreau as early as 1721, at which time it was paired with *Le Défilé*, a scene of military action. If the version of *Le Défilé* in the York City Art Gallery, whose dimensions are virtually identical to those of *La Halte*, is accepted as Watteau's original, then they are a false pair, because it has always been a rectangle, not an oval. The difference in subject-matter and composition also makes it hard to believe in them as pendants, in spite of obvious general similarities. Both represent episodes from military life, and were executed by Watteau after his return to his home town of Valenciennes in 1709. The two victories of the Duke of Marlborough at the Battles of Oudenarde and Malplaquet in July 1708 and September 1709 respectively had the effect of filling nearby Valenciennes with defeated soldiery, and here provided Watteau with his inspiration for a new kind of battle picture that bears no resemblance to the triumphant celebrations of his immediate predecessors. The French soldiers, one of whom has his head bandaged and his left arm in a sling, look distinctly bedraggled. The only accents of colour are provided by a red-coated officer in front of a tent giving orders to his servant, and by the two fashionably dressed ladies who appear to be with him; for the rest, the overall tonality is deliberately drab. The canvas is divided into two by a pair of large spreading trees, and while to the left the distance is blocked off by the tent, to the right there is a background vignette of waggons and of a large pot cooking over a blazing fire.

A number of surviving drawings can be associated with this particular painting, and demonstrate that even at this early stage in his career Watteau had adopted the creative process which he was to maintain for the rest of his short life. This consisted in making countless careful but at the same time spontaneous studies from the life (in this instance all of them are in red chalk), which were subsequently combined in the painting to make satisfying groups and a coherent whole. In a strict sense, therefore, it is not invariably possible to describe sheets as preparatory for particular paintings, and indeed costumes are often changed while poses are retained. Watteau executed a number of these paintings of soldiers for the dealer Sirois, who bought one for 50 *livres*, and gave 200 for a second, but since *La Halte* originally belonged to the artist's biographer, Julienne, it was probably not one of them.

ANTOINE WATTEAU

52. PIERROT CONTENT

Born 1684 in Valenciennes
Died 1721 in Nogent-sur-Marne

Canvas, 35 × 31 cm
Acquired in 1977

This canvas appears to have started out as a copy of a lost painting called *Les Jaloux* ('The Jealous Lovers'), which was exhibited at the Académie des Beaux-Arts in 1712 and whose appearance is known through an engraving. Close inspection of the picture surface of *Pierrot content* shows that Watteau made two significant alterations to his original conception: he painted out some drapery at the feet of the woman holding a fan, and moved her head further away from Pierrot. These two pictures, together with *Arlequin jaloux* and *La Partie quarrée*, are among Watteau's earliest 'Fêtes galantes', representations of characters from the Italian Comedy, or *commedia dell'arte*, which had recently taken Paris by storm.

The central figure of the main group, facing us and clad entirely in white, is Pierrot. He is flanked by two elegantly-dressed women, who are perhaps rivals for his affections. The one to his right looks out at us, plays a small guitar and sings him a song, while the other recoils slightly and rests her fan on her chin. At her feet is another male figure, whom she ignores, seeming instead to look across to the figure of Mezzetin on the other side, who perhaps admires her rival. Behind this tight little group are two additional personages, all but hidden in the undergrowth, over which the profile of a herm of Pan appears to preside. These characters are not easily identified, but they are probably meant for Scaramouche and Harlequin. They are now almost invisible, but an engraving by Edmé Jeurat of 1728 shows them and countless other details considerably more clearly. This print is also the source of the picture's title, and has the further merit of revealing that it has been cut down on both sides. This has had the effect of altering its format from a horizontal to a vertical one, and of removing a block of masonry in the right foreground, which was designed to lead the eye back into the picture space. Possibly the work was cut down because the sides had become indecipherable, and at all events the reason why the remaining foliage has darkened so drastically is that Watteau was an impatient, and perhaps even incompetent technician, who would not wait for the oils to dry before making corrections on the actual canvas. Fortunately, however, in the figure group the shimmering, subtle handling of the draperies, which owes so much to the example of Rubens (cat. 39) and Van Dyck (cat. 20), is virtually intact. No less impressive is the psychological understanding, which is as witty and understated as in the artist's last works. Only in the treatment of the human figure did Watteau make real progress, so that these spindly people appear almost clumsy by comparison with his later achievements.

Pierrot content has recently cast a particularly potent spell over no less an artist than Lucian Freud. Not only did he include it in the background of his portrait of *Baron Hans Heinrich Thyssen-Bornemisza* (fig. 2) but he was inspired by it for the poses of the figure group in his *Large Interior, W.11. (after Watteau)*.

ROGIER VAN DER
WEYDEN
(attributed to)

53. THE VIRGIN AND CHILD

Born 1399 or 1400 in Tournai
Died 1464 in Brussels

Oak panel, 14 × 10.2 cm
Acquired before 1930

This exquisite little panel, which is less than six inches high, almost certainly formed part of a larger whole. Another element, which represents *Saint George and the Dragon*, and whose dimensions are virtually identical, is in the National Gallery of Art in Washington. Here, the Virgin is depicted seated in an elaborate and convincingly three-dimensional architectural niche, which is adorned with elegant Gothic tracery and abundant sculptural decoration. She is flanked by six figures of Old Testament prophets, one of whom—King David—is identifiable by virtue of his usual attributes, the harp and the crown, while up above are seven scenes from the New Testament (the seven Joys of the Virgin). Reading from left to right they are the Annunciation, Visitation, Nativity, Adoration of the Magi, Resurrection and Pentecost, with the Coronation of the Virgin in the centre on a yet higher level. The Virgin's gold and bejewelled crown underlines the fact that she is the Queen of Heaven, but by showing her giving her fully-clothed Son her breast, the artist also stresses both her humility and her humanity. Not all scholars accept this miniature and its companion piece as the work of Rogier van der Weyden, but none would deny that it is clearly from his world. If by him, the dependence of the Virgin's appearance on the comparatively rough-hewn facial types of his master Robert Campin (cat. 32), not to mention the tentativeness of the Child, would both suggest that it is an early work, albeit one that shows awareness of the achievements of Jan van Eyck. The blue of the Virgin's dress and the red of the Child's robe are both well preserved, and their colours are echoed by the jewels in the Virgin's crown. No less beautifully observed are the flowers and grasses to the sides, which reveal the freshness and delicacy of this particular artist's inspiration and of the school of which he is such a distinguished representative.

ROYAL ACADEMY TRUST

Hazlitt Gooden & Fox
The Hedley Foundation
H. J. Heinz Charitable Trust
Mr Henry J. Heinz II
Norman Hepple RA
Herring Son & Daw
Hertz (UK) Ltd
Mr and Mrs Norman Hickman
High Winds Fund
Hill Samuel Group plc
Hilton Hotels Corporation
David Hockney BBC Radio 4 Appeal
Mrs James Stewart Hooker
Ken Howard RA
IBM United Kingdom Group
The Idlewild Trust
Imperial Chemical Industries plc
Imperial Tobacco Limited
Inchcape Charitable Trust
International Hotels Corporation
International Thomson Organization
R. J. Kiln Ltd
Mrs D. King
Kress Foundation
Maurice Laing Foundation
Mr and Mrs Larry Lawrence
Roland P. Lay
Leading Hotels of the World
The Leche Trust
Mr and Mrs Panagiotis Lemos
Mr and Mrs William M. Lese
Lord Leverhulme's Charitable Trust
Mr and Mrs Leon Levy
John Lewis Partnership plc
Lex Services plc
Lloyds Bank plc
The Corporation and Members of Lloyd's
and Lloyd's Brokers
Sir Jack and Lady Lyons
The Manifold Trust
The Manor Charitable Trust
Marks and Spencer plc
Sir George Martin Charitable Trust
Mr and Mrs Jack C. Massey
Matheson & Co. Limited
Paul Mellon KBE
The Anthony and Elizabeth Mellows
   Charitable Trust
The Mercers' Company
The Merchant Taylor's Company
Meridien Hotels Ltd
Midland Bank plc
The Miller and Tiley Charitable Trust
Mobil Oil Company Limited
The Moorgate Trust Fund
Morgan Grenfell & Co. Ltd
National Westminster Bank plc
Mrs Mary Newman
News International plc
Stavros S. Niarchos
Occidental International Oil Inc

Mr and Mrs Peter O'Donnell
H. R. Owen Limited
P&O Steam Navigation Company
Pearson plc
Peerless Pump
Mr and Mrs Milton Petrie
Petrofina UK Ltd
P. F. Charitable Trust
The Pilgrim Trust
The Plessey Company plc
The Private Capital Group
Mr and Mrs Loring G. Pratt
Prudential Assurance Company Limited
Mr and Mrs J. A. Pye's Charitable
   Settlement
The Radcliffe Trust
The Rank Foundation
The Rank Organisation plc
Ranks Hovis McDougall plc
The Rayne Foundation
Reed International plc
The Ronson Charitable Foundation
The Jacob Rothschild Charitable Trust
Rowntree Mackintosh
The Royal Bank of Scotland
RTZ Services Limited
Dr and Mrs Arthur Sackler
The Sainsbury Family Charitable Trust
Jean Sainsbury Charitable Trust
Mr and Mrs Benno C. Schmidt
J. Henry Schroder Wagg & Co Ltd
Peter Samuel Charitable Trust
Mrs Frances Shaile
Mr and Mrs Sam Scali
Sea Containers Limited
Shell UK Limited
Harry & Abe Sherman Foundation
Dr Francis Singer
The Skinners' Company
The Sloane Street Trust
The Sloane Club
Mr Marvin Sloves
Mr and Mrs Edward Byron Smith
Mrs Frederick Stafford
Standard Chartered Bank
Standard Telephones & Cables plc
Mr and Mrs Dennis C. Stanfill
The Starr Foundation
Sterling Guarantee Trust plc
Robert L. Sterling Jr
The Bernard Sunley Charitable Foundation
Tarmac plc
Mr and Mrs A. Alfred Taubman
Technical Indexes Limited
Thames Television Limited
Sir Jules Thorn Charitable Trust
Thorn EMI plc
Thomas Tilling plc
Trafalgar House Limited Company
Mr G. Ware Travelstead
The Triangle Trust (1949) Fund

Trident Television plc
Trustee Savings Bank (Holdings) Limited
TWA
Unilever plc
Veniee Simplon Orient-Express
Vista da Mar Hotel Seychelles
S. G. Warburg & Company Limited
The Wates Foundation
Mrs Keith S. Wellin
Westminster City Council
Anthony Whishaw
Whitbread and Company plc
Wilde Sapte
HDH Wills 1965 Charitable Trust
Winsor and Newton (part of the Reckitt
and Colman Group)
The Wolfson Foundation
Sir John Woolf
Mr Lawrence Wood
Mr Ian Woodner
Mr and Mrs William Wood Prince
Mrs Charles Wrightsman

*Donations to the Appeal should be sent
to the Trust Office at the Royal Academy*

FRIENDS
OF THE ROYAL ACADEMY

Benefactors
Mrs Hilda Benham
Lady Brinton
Sir Nigel & Lady Broackes
Keith Bromley Esq
The John S. Cohen Foundation
The Colby Trust
Michael E. Flintoff Esq
The Lady Gibson
Jack Goldhill Esq FRICS
Mrs Mary Graves
D. J. Hoare Esq
Sir Anthony Hornby
Irene & Hyman Kreitman
The Landmark Trust
Roland Lay Esq
The Trustees of the Leach Fourteenth Trust
Hugh Leggatt Esq
Mr & Mrs M. S. Lipworth
Sir Jack Lyons CBE
The Manor Charitable Trustees
Lieut-Col L. S. Michael OBE
Jan Mitchell Esq
The Lord Moyne
The Lady Moyne
Mrs Sylvia Mulcahy
C. R. Nicholas Esq
Lieut-Col Vincent Paravicini
Mrs Vincent Paravicini
Richard Park Esq
Phillips Fine Art Auctioneers
Mrs Denise Rapp
Mrs Adrianne Reed
The Late Anne M. Roxburgh
Mrs Basil Samuel
Sir Eric Sharp CBE
The Revd Prebendary E. F. Shotter
Dr Francis Singer
Lady Daphne Straight
Mrs Pamela Synge
Harry Teacher Esq
Henry Vyner Charitable Trust
A. Wilkin Vacuum Instruments
   & Products Ltd
Charles Wollaston Esq

*Corporate Sponsors of the Friends and
Members and Associates of the Royal Trust
Corporate Membership Scheme
(to be amalgamated April 1988)*
American Express Europe Ltd
Arthur Anderson & Co
Bankers Trust Company
Barclays Bank plc
Boure Leisure Group Ltd
British Alcan Aluminium Ltd
The British Petroleum Co Ltd
Bryant Laing Partnership
Christie Manson & Woods Ltd
Citibank
Clarkson Jersey Charitable Trust

P & D Colnagi & Co Ltd
Courage Charitable Trust
Couts & Co
Cox Moore plc
Delta Group plc
Esso UK plc
Financial Corporation of North Atlantic Ltd
Ford Motor Company Ltd
The General Electric Company plc
The Granada Group
Grand Metropolitan plc
Arthur Guinness & Sons plc
Guinness Mahon Group plc
Heim Gallery (London) Ltd
IBM United Kingdom Ltd
Imperial Chemical Industries plc
Johnson Wax Limited
Lex Services plc
London Weekend Television Ltd
Marks & Spencer plc
Mars Limited
Martini & Rossi Limited
Worshipful Company of Mercers
Municipal Journal Ltd
Messers Nabarro Nathanson
The Nestlé Charitable Trust
Norddeutsche Landesbank Grozentrale
Ocean Transport & Trading plc
   (P.H. Holt Trust)
Ove Arup Partnership
Pilkington Glass Ltd
Priest Marians Holdings plc
Redfern Gallery
Rowe & Pitman
The Royal Bank of Scotland plc
RTZ Services Limited
Save & Prosper Educational Trust
J. Henry Schroder Wagg & Co Ltd
Scott Mathieson Daines Ltd
Shell UK Limited
W.H. Smith & Son Limited
Sotheby & Co
The Spencer Wills Trust
Thames Television Limited
J. Walter Thompson Company Limited
United Biscuits (UK)

Individual Sponsors
Gerald M. Abraham Esq
Richard Alston Esq
I.F.C. Anstruther Esq
Mrs Anne Appelbe
Dwight W. Arundale Esq
Nick Ashley Esq
Edgar Astaire Esq
Brian A. Bailey Esq
W. M. Ballantyne Esq
Miss Margaret Louise Band
E. P. Bennett Esq
P. F. J. Bennett Esq
Miss A. S. Bergman

SPONSORS OF PAST
EXHIBITIONS

*The Council of the Royal Academy thanks
sponsors of past exhibitions for their support.
Sponsors of major exhibitions during the last
ten years have been included:*

American Express Foundation
Masters of 17th Century Dutch Genre
Painting 1984
'Je suis le cahier': The Sketch Books
of Picasso 1986

Arts Council of Great Britain
Robert Motherwell 1978
Rodrigo Moynihan 1978
John Flaxman 1979
Ivan Hitchens 1979
Algernon Newton 1980
New Spirit in Painting 1981
Gertrude Hermes 1981
Carel Wright 1982
Elizabeth Blackadder 1982
Allan Gwynne Jones 1983
The Hague School 1983
Peter Greenham 1985

BAT Industries plc
Murillo 1983
Paintings from the Royal Academy US Tour
1982/4, RA 1984

Beck's Bier
German Art in the 20th Century 1985

Benson & Hedges
The Gold of El Dorado 1979

Bovis Construction Ltd
New Architecture 1986

British Alcan Aluminium
Sir Alfred Gilbert 1986

British Gypsum Ltd
New Architecture 1986

British Petroleum plc
British Art in the 20th Century 1987

Canary Wharf Development Co
New Architecture 1986

Christie's
Treasures from Chatsworth 1980

Coutts & Co
Derby Day 200 1979

The Daily Telegraph
Treasures from Chatsworth 1980

Deutsche Bank AG
German Art in the 20th Century 1985

Electricity Council
New Architecture 1986

Esso Petroleum Company Ltd
British Art Now: An American Perspective
1980

Financial Times
Derby Day 200 1979

First National Bank of Chicago
Marc Chagall 1985

Friends of the Royal Academy
Elizabeth Blackadder 1982
Carel Wright 1982
Allan Gwynne Jones 1983
Peter Greenham 1985
Sir Alfred Gilbert 1986

Joseph Gartner
New Architecture 1986

Glaxo Holdings plc
From Byzantium to El Greco 1987

Calouste Gulbenkian Foundation
Portuguese Art Since 1910 1978

*Dr Armand Hammer
& The Armand Hammer Foundation*
Honore Daumier 1981
Leonardo da Vinci Nature Studies
Codex Hammer 1981

Hoechst (UK) Ltd
German Art in the 20th Century 1985

IBM United Kingdom Limited
Post-Impressionism 1979
Summer Exhibition 1983

The Japan Foundation
The Great Japan Exhibition 1981

Joannou & Paraskevaides (Overseas) Ltd
From Byzantium to El Greco 1987

Lloyd's Bank
Age of Chivalry 1987

Lufthansa
German Art in the 20th Century 1985

Martini & Rossi Ltd
Painting in Naples from Caravaggio
to Giordano 1982

Melitta
German Art in the 20th Century 1985

Mellon Foundation
Rowlandson Drawings 1978

Mercedes-Benz
German Art in the 20th Century 1985

Midland Bank plc
The Great Japan Exhibition 1981

Mobil
Treasures from Ancient Nigeria 1982
Modern Masters from the Thyssen-
Bornemisza Collection 1984
From Byzantium to El Greco 1987

Möet & Chandon
Derby Day 200 1979

National Westminster Bank
Reynolds 1986

The Observer
Stanley Spencer 1980
The Great Japan Exhibition 1981

Olivetti
Horses of San Marco 1979
The Cimabue Crucifix 1983

The Last Supper 1988

Otis Elevators
New Architecture 1986

Overseas Containers Limited
The Great Japan Exhibition 1981

Pearson plc
Eduardo Paolozzi Underground 1986

Pilkington Glass
New Architecture 1986

Pringle of Scotland
The Great Japan Exhibition 1981

Republic New York Corporation
Andrew Wyeth 1980

Robert Bosch Limited
German Art in the 20th Century 1985

Sea Containers & Venice Simplon Orient Express
Genius of Venice 1983

Shell (UK) Ltd
Treasures from Chatsworth 1980

The Shell Companies of Japan
The Great Japan Exhibition 1981

Siemens
German Art in the 20th Century 1985

Sotheby's
Derby Day 200 1979

Swan Hellenic
Edward Lear 1985

John Swire
The Great Japan Exhibition 1981

Trafalgar House
Elisabeth Frink 1985

Trusthouse Forte
Edward Lear 1985

Unilever
Lord Leverhulme 1980
The Hague School 1983

Walker Books Limited
Edward Lear 1985

Wedgewood
John Flaxman 1979

Winsor & Newton with Reckitt & Colman
Algernon Newton 1980